Functional Analysis

The INTEXT Series
in MATHEMATICS
under the consulting editorship of

RICHARD D. ANDERSON   Louisiana State University
ALEX ROSENBERG   Cornell University

Edward W. Packel

Lake Forest College

Functional Analysis

A Short Course

Intext Educational Publishers   *New York and London*

Library of Congress Cataloging in Publication Data

Packel, Edward W.
Functional analysis.

(Intext series in mathematics)
Includes bibliographical references.
1. Functional analysis.   I.   Title.
QA320.P3   515'.7   73-18337
ISBN 0-7002-2448-3

Intext Educational Publishers
257 Park Avenue South
New York, New York 10010

Text design by Jorge Hernandez

To Lisa and Laura,
my favorite little l's.

Contents

Preface

Experience has convinced me that an appropriately chosen subset of material from the vast and growing field of functional analysis can simultaneously illustrate its beauty, its wealth of application to other areas of mathematics and to physics, and its worth in bringing together in a most natural way standard undergraduate materials in analysis, algebra, and topology. The intended audience for the material in this text can be described as "mathematically mature and motivated undergraduates," which safely covers extremes from precocious juniors to graduate students who have been deprived of the pleasures of modern (clean, soft) analysis. The book assumes a solid background in linear algebra, some experience with metric space and point set topology, facility with complex numbers, and (in the final chapter) a few fundamental results of real and complex analysis. A glance at the Preliminaries should serve to answer more specific questions concerning preparation as well as to illustrate the claim made above about the unifying value of the subject matter.

Chapter 1 introduces the general topological linear space, an excellent setting for uniting and applying two major components of a student's undergraduate background. After developing some of the main ideas, the desirability of having an ample supply of continuous linear functionals motivates the consideration of locally convex spaces. This is the first example of a main theme of the book: a progression from the most general (and least structured) spaces to the specific; this allows the major theorems of the subject to be introduced at the desired level of generality and used thereafter. For example, the Hahn–Banach theorem is proved for a seminorm on a linear space and the Banach–Alaoglu theorem is proved in a locally convex space setting, so the student is made aware that these are not solely theorems about normed linear spaces. Further addition of structure leads to chapters on Banach spaces and Hilbert space, separated by a chapter providing a linear functional approach to integration and measure theory and some fundamental results about L^p spaces. The sixth and final chapter is a brief but self-contained treatment of commutative Banach algebras directed at yielding a spectral theorem for bounded normal operators on Hilbert space. Distribution theory and the interplay between quantum mechanics and Hilbert space (both in simplified form) are two of the major applications that the book considers. Besides being important ideas in their own right, they serve to add meaning to the material for students with a strong interest in physics who invariably seem to help populate and to contribute valuably to courses in functional analysis.

A moderate number of exercises are distributed throughout the text and problems are listed at the end of each chapter. I have made a special effort to use results that will be truly instructive, and the exercises, which may take the form of requests to provide proofs that are omitted, were chosen specifically to develop the student's facility with the concepts just introduced. The student should attempt and have some success with almost all of the exercises, and the hints given to make this claim reasonable should be ignored if possible.

The material included here has been used with groups of undergraduates in one-semester courses at Reed College and Lake Forest College. A brisk pace should make it possible to cover the book in its entirety in one semester, and omission of Chapter 4 or Chapter 6 allows a more leisurely pace. Chapters 1, 2, 3, and 5 form the nucleus of the book and (excepting proofs of results on L^p spaces from Chapter 4) are self-contained.

As is often the case, the seeds of many of the ideas appearing here were planted by influential teachers and books. In particular, the approach and subject matter chosen have been strongly influenced by Kenneth M. Hoffman, the author's teacher at M.I.T. Simmons' excellent text, *Introduction to Topology and Modern Analysis,* is also an important part of the author's past and has no doubt left its mark on the style and content of what follows. Lastly, the material in Chapter 4 leans heavily upon and expands the Daniell integral development found in Loomis' book, *Abstract Harmonic Analysis.*

The author wishes to thank all students who participated in the evolution of this book. Their compliments, criticisms, and general comments have been an important part of the writing process. Special thanks are due to Carter Hinckley for his careful scrutiny of the text at all stages from classroom notes to page proofs. My good friend and former colleague Jack Cook read the whole manuscript at a crucial time, smoked out errors unmercifully, and made a number of valuable suggestions about content. Peggy Davidson (typing) and Doreen Packel (proofreading) must also be cited for their courageous performances under the pressure of time. The author is grateful to Lake Forest College for financial assistance and general encouragement, and to the Mathematical Institute, Oxford, for providing the exceedingly pleasant setting in which the book took shape. Finally, the author wishes to thank the staff at Intext Educational Publishers for their insight, patience, and cooperation.

Symbols

$\mathcal{A}(D)$	analytic functions on D
$\mathcal{A}(\overline{D})$	functions analytic on D, continuous on $\overline{D}$
$\overline{B}$	$\mathbf{R}^e$ –valued functions obtainable as increasing limits from $\mathcal{L}$
$\underline{B}$	$\mathbf{R}^e$ –valued functions obtainable as decreasing limits from $\mathcal{L}$
$\mathcal{B}$	Baire functions obtained from $\mathcal{L}$
$\mathcal{B}^+$	nonnegative Baire functions
$\mathcal{B}^-$	nonpositive Baire functions
$\mathcal{B}(X, Y)$	continuous linear transformations from X to Y
$\mathcal{B}(X)$	bounded linear operators on X
$\mathrm{CH}(U)$	convex hull of U
$\mathbf{C}$	field of complex numbers
$\mathcal{C}_K^\infty(\mathbf{R}^n)$	infinitely differentiable functions on $\mathbf{R}^n$ vanishing outside K
$\mathcal{C}_0^\infty(\mathbf{R}^n)$	infinitely differentiable functions on $\mathbf{R}^n$ vanishing outside some compact set
$\mathcal{C}(S)$	bounded continuous functions on a topological space S with sup norm
D	open complex unit disk
$\overline{D}$	closure of D
D_f	variance corresponding to density function f
$D_\psi(A)$	variance associated with observable A in state ψ
$\mathcal{D}(\mathbf{R}^n)$	$\mathcal{C}_0^\infty(\mathbf{R}^n)$ with inductive limit topology—test functions
δ_{ij}	Kronecker delta
Δ	nonzero algebra homomorphisms on a Banach algebra
$(E; \leq)$	partially ordered set under the relation $\leq$
E_f	expected value corresponding to density function f
$E_\psi(A)$	expected value associated with observable A in state ψ
G	regular elements in a Banach algebra with identity
H	Heaviside function; Hilbert space
I	index set; integral on a linear lattice $\mathcal{L}$
Im	imaginary part
$\ker(f)$	kernel of function f
$\mathbf{K}$	field of real or complex numbers

l^2	square summable sequences
$l^2(\mathcal{Z})$	two-way square summable sequences
l^p	pth power summable sequences
l^∞	bounded sequences with the sup norm
L^p	equivalence classes of pth power summable functions
$L^p(I)$	L^p space arising from the integral I
$L^p(S)$	L^p space arising from functions on a set S with Lebesgue measure
L^∞	equivalence classes of essentially bounded functions from $\mathcal{B}$
$\mathcal{L}$	linear lattice of functions on a set S
$\mathcal{L}^1$	summable functions with respect to $\mathcal{L}$
$\mathcal{L}^p$	pth power summable functions
$\mathcal{L}^\infty$	essentially bounded functions from $\mathcal{B}$
μ	measure on a σ-algebra
$\mathfrak{M}$	maximal ideal space of a Banach algebra
P	momentum operator on $L^2(\mathbf{R})$
Q	position operator on $L^2(\mathbf{R})$
$r(x)$	spectral radius of x
R	radical in a Banach algebra
R_x	resolvent function for x
Re	real part
$\mathbf{R}$	field of real numbers
$\mathbf{R}^e$	extended real numbers
ρ	seminorm on a linear space
$\rho(x)$	resolvent set of x
sgn	signum function
S	singular elements in a Banach algebra with identity
$\mathcal{S}$	σ-algebra of subsets of a set S
$\sigma(x)$	spectrum of Banach algebra element x
T^*	adjoint of linear mapping T
T_δ	Dirac δ distribution
T_ϕ	distribution function for the function ϕ
$\hat{x}$	member of X^{**} arising from x in X
$\hat{X}$	image of X in X^{**} under $\wedge$
X^*	conjugate space of X
X_w	X with the weak topology

X_w^*	weak* topology on X^*
X_s^*	strong topology on X^*
χ_A	characteristic function of the set A
$\cong$	isomorphism
$\perp$	annihilator; orthogonal complement
$\circ$	polar
$*$	complex conjugate; conjugate space; adjoint
$\wedge$	natural map from X to X^{**}; Gelfand map
$\| \ \|$	norm
$\| \ \|_p$	L^p norm
$\| \ \|_\infty$	(essential) sup norm
$< , >$	inner product
$\oplus$	direct sum
$\times$	Cartesian product
$\vee$	maximum operation on lattice of functions
$\wedge$	minimum operation on lattice of functions

Functional Analysis

Preliminaries

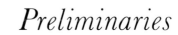

This preliminary chapter is intended to outline notation, concepts, and theorems that will be used without full development or proof in the following six chapters. It should serve as a guide to what the reader should either already know or be prepared to acquire when the need arises rather than as a list of concepts and theorems to be studied and mastered before beginning. Thus an effort has been made to present prerequisite concepts and theorems where they naturally arise in the text in addition to mentioning them here. Notation and basic terminology used are for the most part either standard or self-explanatory, and the meaning of such familiar concepts as $A \cap B$, $f: X \rightarrow Y$, $\{x \in X : x$ has property $p\}$, and *subsequence* will not be reviewed. The reader will find all concepts and results mentioned below discussed fully in, for example, Simmons' book [1], with the exception of the material on complex analysis which can be found in any introductory text on that subject.

□ SET THEORY

The language of elementary set theory is used freely throughout the book. The *complement* of a subset A of a universe set S is denoted by A' and $B \backslash A = \{x \in S : x \in B$ and $x \notin A\}$. The *Cartesian product* $A_1 \times A_2$ of two sets A_1 and A_2 generalizes to the product $\Pi_{\alpha \in I} A_\alpha$ of a collection of sets $\{A_\alpha\}_{\alpha \in I}$ indexed by any index set I. This product may be thought of as the set of all functions f defined on I and satisfying $f(\alpha) \in X_\alpha$ for each $\alpha \in I$. *Sequences* are denoted by $\{f_i\}$, or $\{f_i\}_{i=1}^{\infty}$ if a clearer specification of the domain is required. The *Kronecker delta* δ_{ij} denotes the value 1 if $i = j$ and 0 otherwise, and the *signum function* sgn is defined on **R** by

$$\operatorname{sgn}(x) = \begin{cases} 1 & \text{if } x > 0 \\ -1 & \text{if } x < 0 \\ 0 & \text{if } x = 0. \end{cases}$$

Greatest lower bounds and least upper bounds are denoted by inf and sup respectively. The concept of an *equivalence relation* on a set and the decomposition of a set into disjoint *equivalence classes* is used several times. *Partial order relations, partially ordered sets,* and *Zorn's lemma* are defined and briefly developed in Chapter 1, and are needed in Chapters 1, 5, and 6. The concept of *countable* and *uncountable* sets arises in various settings and familiarity with the idea is assumed. More general *cardinality* results are needed and used at one point in Chapter 5.

□ **TOPOLOGY**

Familiarity with *topological space, open set, interior, closed set, compact set, continuous function, relative topology,* and other elementary topological notions is assumed. If the open sets of one topological space are a subcollection of the open sets of a second, the topology on the first space is *weaker* than the topology on the second. The *indiscrete* topology admits only the empty set and the whole space as open, while the *discrete* topology accepts all subsets as open. A *dense* subset of a topological space X is a set whose closure equals X. A *separable* topological space is one that has a countable dense subset. A *neighborhood* of a point is taken to be a set whose interior contains the point, and a *neighborhood base* at a point p is a collection of neighborhoods of p such that every open set containing p is a superset of some neighborhood from the collection. An *open base* (*neighborhood base*) for a topology is a collection of open sets (neighborhoods) such that every open set is a union of sets from the open base (neighborhood base). An *open subbase* is a collection of open sets whose finite intersections form an open base. A topological space is *first countable* if it has a countable neighborhood base at each point, and is *second countable* if it has a countable neighborhood base. The presence of either of these countability conditions allows the use of sequential arguments for continuity of functions and closedness of sets. Given a collection of functions $f_\alpha: X \to Y_\alpha$ where X is a set and the $\{Y_\alpha\}_{\alpha \in I}$ are topological spaces, the *weak topology* on X generated by the $\{f_\alpha\}$ is the weakest topology on X for which all f_α are continuous, and the sets

$$f_\alpha^{-1}(V) = \{x \in X : f_\alpha(x) \in V\} \qquad (\alpha \in I, \quad V \text{ open in } Y_\alpha)$$

form an open subbase for the weak topology on X. Given a collection $\{X_\alpha\}_{\alpha \in I}$ of topological spaces, the *product topology* on $\Pi_{\alpha \in I} X_\alpha$ is the weak topology generated by the *projection mappings* $p_\beta:$ $\Pi_{\alpha \in I} X_\alpha \to X_\beta$ defined by $p_\beta(f) = f(\beta)$. An open base for this topology consists of all sets $\Pi_{\alpha \in I} G_\alpha$ where the $\{G_\alpha\}$ are open sets with $G_\alpha = X_\alpha$ for all but finitely many indices α. *Tychonoff's theorem* states that a product of compact topological spaces is compact. The elementary theory of *metric spaces* is assumed as is the *Baire category theorem,* which states that a complete metric space cannot be expressed as a countable union of closed sets with empty interior.

□ ALGEBRA

The concept of a *vector space* over **R** or **C** is defined at the outset of Chapter 1, but basic ideas from linear algebra are used freely and without prior definition. Notions like *subspace, linear combination, basis,* and *linear transformation* are omnipresent. Chapter 6 defines an *algebra,* uses *homomorphisms* and *kernels* freely, and introduces *ideals I* and *maximal ideals* in a commutative algebra *A* with *identity.* It is asserted without proof that the *quotient space A/I* has a natural commutative algebra structure and becomes a commutative *division algebra* (nonzero elements are invertible) and hence a *field* when *I* is a maximal ideal.

□ ANALYSIS

Familiarity with elementary real-variable concepts is assumed, as is a facility with complex numbers and the idea of a complex-valued function. The notation $\mathrm{Re}(z)$ and $\mathrm{Im}(z)$ is used to denote the real and imaginary parts of a complex number z, and z^* denotes the complex conjugate of z. A complex-valued function is *analytic* (or *holomorphic*) on a domain D of the complex plane if

$$f'(z_0) = \lim_{z \to z_0} \frac{f(z) - f(z_0)}{z - z_0}$$

exists for all z_0 in D. The well-known result that two analytic functions with domain D which agree on a nonempty open set must agree on all of D is needed in an exercise in Chapter 2. Beyond this no significant use of complex analysis is made until Chapter 6, where the following standard results of real and complex analysis are used without proof:

1. The *Liouville theorem:* A complex-valued function that is analytic and bounded on all of the complex plane must be a constant.

2. A complex-valued function g defined and analytic on the complement of a closed disk centered at the origin of the complex plane has a unique *Laurent expansion* on its domain of the form $g(z) = \sum_{k=0}^{\infty} \alpha_k z^{-k}$.

3. The *Weierstrass approximation theorem:* The polynomials on a compact subset K of **R** are dense (with respect to the sup norm topology) in the algebra of continuous real-valued functions on K.

4. The *complex Stone–Weierstrass theorem:* Let A be a subalgebra of the continuous complex-valued functions on a compact Hausdorff space S such that A separates points of S, contains a nonzero constant function, and is closed under conjugation of functions. Then A is dense.

Topological Linear Spaces

1

☐ INTRODUCTORY REMARKS

The discipline of functional analysis has its origins in the incurable yet vital tendency mathematicians have for axiomatization and generalization as applied to the ideas of classical analysis. While the beginnings of this "abstract analysis" can be traced back into the nineteenth century, recognition as an important new mathematical discipline had to wait until the 1930s when Von Neumann's mathematization of quantum mechanics as well as several clean and concise proofs of important but laborious classical results secured its claims. Initially viewed as studying common and distinguishing properties of various spaces of functions (in contrast to the old practice of examining the functions individually), functional analysis can now be thought of as emanating from a marriage of linear algebra and topology, resulting in the concept of a topological linear space. Accordingly we begin our study with this fundamental concept which, when combined with increasingly specialized assumptions, will lead to various increasingly specialized spaces and results. It should be mentioned that our study will involve only *linear* functional analysis whose relation to the newly developing nonlinear theory is analogous to and stems from the relation between Euclidean spaces and manifolds.

☐ DEFINITIONS AND BASIC PROPERTIES

Let $\mathbf{K}$ denote either the field of real numbers $\mathbf{R}$ or the field of complex numbers $\mathbf{C}$. A *linear space* X is a vector space over $\mathbf{K}$. Thus X is nonempty, closed under an "addition" and under a "multiplication" by scalars from $\mathbf{K}$, and the following axioms are satisfied for all $x, y, z \in X$ and $\alpha, \beta \in \mathbf{K}$.

(1) $x + y = y + x$.
(2) $x + (y + z) = (x + y) + z$.
(3) X has an additive identity which we denote by 0.
(4) Each $x \in X$ has an additive inverse which we denote by $-x$.
(5) $\alpha(\beta x) = (\alpha\beta)x$.
(6) $(\alpha + \beta)x = \alpha x + \beta x$.
(7) $\alpha(x + y) = \alpha x + \alpha y$.
(8) $1 \cdot x = x$ where 1 is the multiplicative identity in $\mathbf{K}$.

We now define several important kinds of subsets of a linear space X; each of these has a natural geometric interpretation in the linear space $\mathbf{C}$. Let U denote a subset of X.

U is (*point*) *absorbing* if for every $x \in X$ there is an $r > 0$ such that $\alpha x \in U$ for all $\alpha \in \mathbf{K}$ with $|\alpha| \le r$. Note that $|\cdot|$ denotes the absolute value on $\mathbf{R}$ and the modulus on $\mathbf{C}$.

U is *balanced* if $\alpha U \subset U$ whenever $|\alpha| \le 1$. Note

$$\alpha U = \{\alpha u \in X : u \in U\}.$$

U is *convex* if $x, y \in U \Rightarrow tx + (1 - t)y \in U$ for all $t \in [0, 1].$,

The *convex hull* $\mathrm{CH}(U)$ of U is the intersection of all convex sets containing U. Note that X itself is one such convex set.

EXERCISE 1.1   a. Prove that $\{U_i\}_{i \in I}$ balanced $\Rightarrow \bigcap_{i \in I} U_i$ is balanced, and that U balanced and $\beta \in \mathbf{K} \Rightarrow \beta U$ balanced.

b. Repeat (a) with balanced replaced by convex. This shows in particular that for any $U \subset X$, $\mathrm{CH}(U)$ is the smallest convex set containing U.

c. Show that the set defined in polar coordinates by

$$S = \{(r, \theta) : 0 \le r \le 2\pi - \theta, 0 \le \theta < 2\pi\}$$

is an absorbing subset of $\mathbf{R}^2$, but is not an absorbing subset of $\mathbf{C}$ ($\mathbf{R}^2$ endowed with complex scalar multiplication).

LEMMA 1.1   For any $U \subset X$,

$$\mathrm{CH}(U) = \left\{ x \in X : x = \sum_{i=1}^{n} t_i u_i, \quad u_i \in U, \quad t_i > 0, \quad \sum_{i=1}^{n} t_i = 1 \right\}.$$

□ **PROOF**   Let the set to the right of the equal sign be denoted by S, and we shall prove that $\mathrm{CH}(U) = S$. It is readily seen that $U \subset S$, and the convexity of X is shown by the following natural calculation: Let x and y belong to S, so that $x = \sum_{i=1}^{n} t_i u_i$ and $y = \sum_{j=1}^{m} s_j v_j$ with all the appropriate conditions on t_i, u_i, s_j, and v_j. Then

$$tx + (1 - t)y = \sum_{i=1}^{n} tt_i u_i + \sum_{j=1}^{m} (1 - t)s_j v_j$$

and

$$\sum_{i=1}^{n} tt_i + \sum_{j=1}^{m} (1 - t)s_j = t \cdot 1 + (1 - t) \cdot 1 = 1,$$

so $tx + (1 - t)y \in S$ and S is convex. Since S is a convex set containing U, the definition of $CH(U)$ yields $CH(U) \subseteq S$. To establish the reverse inclusion, let $x = \sum_{i=1}^{n} t_i u_i$ be in S, and we shall show by induction on n that $x \in CH(U)$. As usual the $n = 1$ case is immediate, and assuming the result for a general n, consider $x \in S$ where $x = \sum_{i=1}^{n+1} s_i v_i, \in U, s_i > 0, \sum_{i=1}^{n+1} s_i = 1$. Since $s_{n+1} \neq 1$, we can write

$$x = (1 - s_{n+1}) \sum_{i=1}^{n} \frac{s_i}{1 - s_{n+1}} v_i + s_{n+1} v_{n+1}.$$

Since $\sum_{i=1}^{n} s_i = 1 - s_{n+1}$,

$$\sum_{i=1}^{n} \frac{s_i}{1 - s_{n+1}} v_i$$

belongs to S and hence to $CH(U)$ by the induction hypothesis. Finally, by the convexity of $CH(U)$ (Exercise 1.1b) we conclude that $x \in CH(U)$, completing the proof.

EXERCISE 1.2　a. Prove that the convex hull of a balanced set is balanced.

b. Prove that for a subset U of X it is not generally true that $\frac{1}{2}U + \frac{1}{2}U = U$　$(\frac{1}{2}U + \frac{1}{2}U = \{\frac{1}{2}u_1 + \frac{1}{2}u_2 : u_1, u_2 \in U\})$.

c. Prove that if U is convex, the result in (b) is true and, more generally, $\sum_{i=1}^{n} (t_i U) = (\sum_{i=1}^{n} t_i) U$ for any $t_1, t_2, \ldots, t_n \geq 0$.

Before presenting the very natural idea of a topological linear space, we briefly recall the definition of a topological space.

A *topological space* (X, τ) is a set X together with a collection τ of *open* subsets of X (called the topology on X) satisfying:

1. $\emptyset \in \tau$ and $X \in \tau$.
2. τ is closed under finite intersection.
3. τ is closed under arbitrary union.

A *topological linear space* (tls) is a linear space X together with a topology on X with respect to which

1. Addition is continuous: $X \times X \to X$, $(x, y) \mapsto x + y$.
2. Scalar multiplication is continuous: $\mathbf{K} \times X \to X$, $(\alpha, x) \mapsto \alpha x$, where $\mathbf{K}$ is assumed to have the Euclidean topology and the product topologies are used for $X \times X$ and $\mathbf{K} \times X$.

While it is tempting to deal with continuity of the operations on a tls in terms of inverse images of open sets remaining open, it will be more convenient in what follows to use the equivalent idea of pointwise continuity at every point in the domain. Thus continuity of addition at $(x, y) \in X \times X$ means that for any neighborhood W of $x + y$ (i.e., $x + y$ is in the interior of W) there exist neighborhoods U of x and V of y such that $+(U \times V) = U + V \subseteq W$, where $U + V = \{u + v \in X : u \in U \text{ and } v \in V\}$. A similar remark applies to scalar multiplication. It follows readily that in a tls the translation functions $T_x : y \in X \mapsto x + y \in X$ and the multiplication functions $M_\alpha : x \in X \mapsto \alpha x \in X$ $(\alpha \in \mathbf{K}, \alpha \neq 0)$ are homeomorphisms. A further important consequence is that in discussing tls topologies it is sufficient to concentrate on the neighborhoods of $0 \in X$, for U is a neighborhood of 0 if and only if $x + U$ is a neighborhood of x.

THEOREM 1.2   Let X be a tls and $\mathfrak{F}$ a neighborhood base at 0 for the topology on X. Then

a. $U, V \in \mathfrak{F} \Rightarrow$ there exists $W \in \mathfrak{F}$ such that $W \subseteq U \cap V$.
b. $U \in \mathfrak{F} \Rightarrow$ there exists $V \in \mathfrak{F}$ such that $V + V \subseteq U$.
c. $U \in \mathfrak{F} \Rightarrow U$ is absorbing, so neighborhoods of 0 are always absorbing.
d. $U \in \mathfrak{F}$ and $r > 0 \Rightarrow$ there exists $V \in \mathfrak{F}$ such that $\alpha V \subseteq U$ for all $|\alpha| \leq r$.
e. The topology on X is Hausdorff $\Leftrightarrow \bigcap_{U \in \mathfrak{F}} U = \{0\}$.

Conversely, let X be a linear space and $\mathfrak{F}$ a nonempty collection of subsets of X satisfying (a)–(d). Then defining A to be open if for each $x \in A$ there exists $U \in \mathfrak{F}$ such that $x + U \subseteq A$, a topology is obtained with respect to which X is a tls and $\mathfrak{F}$ a neighborhood base at 0.

□   **PROOF**   Assume first that X is a tls and $\mathfrak{F}$ a neighborhood base at 0.

(a) This is a fundamental property of a neighborhood base at a point.

(b) Using $0 + 0 = 0$ and the continuity of addition, since U is a neighborhood of 0, there must exist neighborhoods V_1 and V_2 of 0 such that $V_1 + V_2 \subseteq U$. Since $\mathfrak{F}$ is a neighborhood base at 0, there exists $V \in \mathfrak{F}$ such that $V \subseteq V_1 \cap V_2$ and we obtain

$$V + V \subseteq U.$$

(c) Using $0 \cdot x = 0 \in U$ and the continuity of multiplication (with emphasis on the neighborhood of the scalar 0), we obtain $\epsilon > 0$ such that $|\alpha| < \epsilon \Longrightarrow \alpha x \in U$.

(d) Given $U \in \mathfrak{F}$ and any $\alpha \in \mathbf{K}$ with $|\alpha| \le r$, use of $\alpha \cdot 0 = 0 \in U$ and the continuity of scalar multiplication ensure the existence of neighborhoods N_α of α in $\mathbf{K}$ and V_α of 0 in X such that $N_\alpha V_\alpha \subseteq U$. Since $\bar{D}_r = \{\alpha \in \mathbf{K} : |\alpha| \le r\}$ is compact, there exist $\alpha_1, \alpha_2, \ldots, \alpha_n$ such that $\bar{D}_r \subseteq \bigcup_{i=1}^n N_{\alpha_i}$. Choosing $V \in \mathfrak{F}$ such that $V \subseteq \bigcap_{i=1}^n V_{\alpha_i}$. we have $|\alpha| \le r \Longrightarrow \alpha \in \bar{D}_r \Longrightarrow \alpha \in N_{\alpha_j}$ for some $j \Longrightarrow \alpha V \subseteq N_{\alpha_j} V_{\alpha_j} \subseteq U$.

(e) $\Longrightarrow$: Follows directly from the definition of Hausdorff. $\Longleftarrow$: Since translations are homeomorphisms, it suffices, given $0 \in X$ and an arbitrary $x \ne 0$, to find disjoint neighborhoods of these two points. First find $W \in \mathfrak{F}$ such that $x \notin W$. Choose $V \in \mathfrak{F}$ such that $V + V \subseteq W$ using (b). Then V is a neighborhood of 0 and $x - V = \{y \in X : y = x - v, v \in V\}$ is a neighborhood of x (why?). Furthermore, $V \cap (x - V) = \emptyset$ since otherwise there would exist $v_1, v_2 \in V$ such that $v_1 = x - v_2$ from which results the contradiction that $x = v_1 + v_2 \in W$. For the "conversely" part of the theorem, it is readily checked using (a) that the definition of open does indeed provide a topology and that $\mathfrak{F}$ is a neighborhood base for the topology. Continuity of addition proceeds as follows: Given $x, y \in X$ and a neighborhood W of $x + y$, then $W - (x + y)$ is a neighborhood of 0, so there exists $U \in \mathfrak{F}$ with $U \subseteq W - (x + y)$. By (b) there exists $V \in \mathfrak{F}$ such that $V + V \subseteq U \subseteq W - (x + y)$. Hence $(x + V) + (y + V) \subseteq W$ so addition is continuous at $(x, y) \in X \times X$. Continuity of scalar multiplication is trickier and will be seen to follow from an abstract form of an "$\epsilon/3$ argument" plus judicious use of (b), (c), and (d). Given $x \in X$, $\alpha \in \mathbf{K}$ ($\alpha \ne 0$) (the $\alpha = 0$ case is immediate since constant functions are always continuous), and a neighborhood W of αx, repeated use of (b) yields a $U \in \mathfrak{F}$ such that $U + U + U + U \subseteq W - \alpha x$, from which we certainly obtain $U + U + U \subseteq W - \alpha x$ since $0 \in U$.

Using (d) with $r = |\alpha|$ and letting $\bar{D}_r = \{\beta \in \mathbf{K} : |\beta| \le r\}$, we obtain $V \in \mathfrak{F}$ such that $\bar{D}_r V \subseteq U$. Since, by (c), U is absorbing we obtain a neighborhood $\bar{D}_\epsilon$ of 0 in $\mathbf{K}$ such that $\bar{D}_\epsilon x \subseteq V$. Letting $\delta = \min\{\epsilon, r\}$ we obtain

$$\bar{D}_\delta V + \bar{D}_\delta x + \alpha V \subseteq U + U + U \subseteq W - \alpha x$$
$$\Rightarrow \bar{D}_\delta V + \bar{D}_\delta x + \alpha V + \alpha x \subseteq W$$
$$\Rightarrow (\bar{D}_\delta + \alpha)(V + x) \subseteq W,$$

establishing continuity of scalar multiplication at $(\alpha, x) \in \mathbf{K} \times X$ and completing the proof.

EXERCISE 1.3   a. Is a linear space with the discrete topology a tls?

b. Is a linear space with the indiscrete topology a tls?

The following theorem illustrates the interplay between the linear and topological concepts in a tls. A bar over a subset denotes its closure.

THEOREM 1.3   Let X be a tls. Then

a. $\overline{x + A} = x + \bar{A}$ and $\overline{\alpha A} = \alpha \bar{A}, \alpha \ne 0$.

b. If U is open and $A \subseteq X$, then $A + U$ is open.

c. $\bar{A} + \bar{B} \subseteq \overline{A + B}$.

d. If C and D are compact, then $C + D$ is compact.

e. If A is any subset of X, $\bar{A} = \cap (A + U)$, as U ranges over all neighborhoods of 0.

f. The closure of a convex set is convex.

g. The closure of a (linear) subspace of X is a subspace.

h. Every neighborhood of 0 contains a balanced neighborhood of 0.

i. Every convex neighborhood of 0 contains a convex balanced neighborhood of 0.

□ **PROOF**

(a)

$$y \in \overline{x + A} \Leftrightarrow \text{every neighborhood of } y \text{ intersects } x + A$$
$$\Leftrightarrow \text{every neighborhood of } y - x \text{ intersects } A$$
$$\Leftrightarrow y - x \in \bar{A}$$
$$\Leftrightarrow y \in x + \bar{A}.$$

The argument for $\overline{\alpha A} = \alpha\bar{A}$, $\alpha \neq 0$, is similar.

(b) $A + U = \bigcup_{x \in A}(x + U)$ which is open as a union of open sets.

(c) $x \in \bar{A} + \bar{B} \Rightarrow x = a + b$, where every neighborhood of a intersects A and every neighborhood of b intersects B. By continuity of addition it follows that every neighborhood of $a + b$ intersects $A + B$, so $x = a + b \in \overline{A + B}$.

(d) $C + D$ is compact as the continuous image (under $+$) of the compact set $C \times D$.

(e) $x \in \bigcap (A + U) \Longleftrightarrow (x - U) \cap A \neq \emptyset$ for all neighborhoods U of $0 \Longleftrightarrow x \in \bar{A}$.

(f) Let C be convex and let $x, y \in \bar{C}$. We will show that for any neighborhood U of 0 and any $t \in (0,1)$, $tx + (1 - t)y \in C + U$. This coupled with (e) will yield the desired result. Using Theorem 1.2b, choose a neighborhood V of 0 such that $V + V \subseteq U$. Since $x, y \in \bar{C}$, (e) yields $x \in C + (1/t)V$ and $y \in C + 1/(1 - t)V$. Hence

$$tx + (1 - t)y \in tC + (1 - t)C + V + V \subseteq C + U,$$

where the convexity of C and Exercise 1.2c have been used in replacing $tC + (1 - t)C$ by C.

(g) This follows by an argument very similar to that used for (f).

(h) From Theorem 1.2d, if U is a neighborhood of 0, then there exists a neighborhood V of 0 such that $\alpha V \subseteq U$ for all α with $|\alpha| \leq 1$. Defining $W = \bigcup_{|\alpha| \leq 1}(\alpha V)$, we have $W \subseteq U$ and W balanced.

(i) Given a convex neighborhood U of 0, obtain W as in (h) and set $Y = CH(W)$. Then $Y \subseteq U$ since U is convex, and Y is balanced by Exercise 1.2 b.

□ **EXAMPLES**

We now introduce some general and specific examples of topological linear spaces. The examples are meant to provide the reader with a preview of three very important kinds of spaces that are studied in functional analysis and in this text. A solid mastery of all the ideas introduced is not required at this time. That each general type of space is a tls can be shown using Theorem 1.2, but each will be dealt with more specifically as it arises in a later chapter.

□ **EXAMPLE 1**   A *seminorm* on the linear space X is a function $\rho: X \to \mathbf{R}$ such that for all $x, y \in X$ and $\alpha \in \mathbf{K}$

(a) $\rho(\alpha x) = |\alpha| \rho(x)$
(b) $\rho(x + y) \leq \rho(x) + \rho(y)$ (triangle inequality)
(c) $\rho(x) \geq 0$.

If ρ also satisfies

(d) $\rho(x) = 0 \Rightarrow x = 0$

then ρ becomes a *norm* on X.

Let $\{\rho_i\}_{i \in I}$ be a collection of seminorms on X for some index set I. Topologize X with the weakest topology such that all ρ_i are continuous. Then X becomes a tls (and even better, as we shall see, a *locally convex tls*).

A neighborhood subbase at 0 for the tls X is the collection of subsets of X of the form

$$U_{i,\epsilon} = \{x \in X : \rho_i(x) < \epsilon\} \quad (i \in I, \quad \epsilon > 0).$$

Recall that the set of all finite intersections of this subbase at 0 is a neighborhood base at 0.

As an example of this example, let D denote the *open* unit disk in $\mathbf{C}$ and let $\mathbf{\mathfrak{A}}(D) = \{$analytic functions on $D\}$. Clearly $\mathbf{\mathfrak{A}}(D)$ is a complex linear space and if we define for each compact subset K of D

$$\rho_K(f) = \sup_{z \in K} |f(z)| \quad (f \in \mathbf{\mathfrak{A}}(D)),$$

then each ρ_K is a seminorm on $\mathbf{\mathfrak{A}}(D)$. The weak topology generated by all the ρ_K makes $\mathbf{\mathfrak{A}}(D)$ a tls. Topologies of this sort are sometimes called *compact–open* topologies (why?) and $f_n \to f$ in this topology turns out to mean that f_n converges uniformly to f on all compact subsets of D. Thus the topology is also referred to as the topology of *uniform convergence on compact sets*.

□ **EXAMPLE 2**   Let X be a linear space that is topologized as above by just one norm. Then X is called a *normed linear space*. If

X is complete (every Cauchy sequence converges) with respect to the metric induced by this norm (see Exercise 1.4), X is called a *Banach space*.

As a concrete example, $\mathcal{C}([0,1])$ = {continuous **K**-valued functions on $[0,1]$} is a Banach space if the norm is chosen as

$$\rho(f) = \|f\| = \sup_{x \in [0,1]} |f(x)|.$$

The concepts of seminorm and norm just introduced will very soon be playing a vital role in our development, and the reader should become familiar with their defining properties.

EXERCISE 1.4 a. Show that a norm $\|\ \|$ on a linear space X induces a metric d on X by $d(x,y) = \|x - y\|$.

b. Show that for a norm on X the familiar metric space definition of completeness reduces to: $\lim_{m,n\to\infty} \|x_n - x_m\| = 0 \Rightarrow$ there exists $x \in X$ such that $\lim_{n\to\infty} \|x - x_n\| = 0$ (i.e. $x_n \to x$).

c. Show that $\|f\| = \sup_{x \in [0,1]} |f(x)|$ is indeed a norm on $\mathcal{C}([0,1])$. It is called the *sup* or *uniform norm*, and gives rise to uniform convergence on $[0,1]$.

d. Prove $\mathcal{C}([0,1])$ is complete with respect to the sup norm given above. Hints for (d):

i. If $\{f_n\}$ is the Cauchy sequence, use the completeness of **K** to obtain a candidate f for the limit of the Cauchy sequence.

ii. Show that $\|f - f_n\| \to 0$ by means of the inequality

$$|f(x) - f_n(x)| \le |f(x) - f_m(x)| + |f_m(x) - f_n(x)|.$$

iii. Show that $f \in \mathcal{C}([0,1])$ by applying the triangle inequality twice to $|f(x) - f(x_0)|$ and using (ii).

□ **EXAMPLE 3**   An *inner product* on X is a function $\langle,\rangle : X \times X \to$ **K** such that

(a) $\langle x,y\rangle = \langle y,x\rangle^*$ (where * denotes complex conjugation).
(b) $\langle \alpha x + \beta y, z\rangle = \alpha\langle x,z\rangle + \beta\langle y,z\rangle$.
(c) $\langle x,x\rangle \ge 0$ for all x; and $\langle x,x\rangle = 0 \Rightarrow x = 0$.

We will show later that $\|x\| = \langle x,x\rangle^{1/2}$ defines a norm on X, and topologizing X with this norm makes it an *inner product space*. If X is complete, then X is called a *Hilbert space*.

Thus $\mathbf{K}^n$, the n-fold Cartesian product of $\mathbf{K}$ with itself, is a (finite-dimensional) Hilbert space via the inner product

$$\langle x, y \rangle = \sum_{i=1}^{n} x_i y_i^*,$$

where $x = (x_1, \ldots, x_n)$ and $y = (y_1, \ldots, y_n)$.

□ **LINEAR TRANSFORMATIONS AND LINEAR FUNCTIONALS**

Invariably in the study of a collection (category) of mathematical objects it is fruitful to investigate the set of mappings (morphisms) from one such object to another which preserve some or all of the structure defined on the objects. If X and Y are topological linear spaces over the same field $\mathbf{K}$, a *linear transformation* is a map $T: X \to Y$ such that

$$T(\alpha_1 x_1 + \alpha_2 x_2) = \alpha_1 T x_1 + \alpha_2 T x_2$$

for all $\alpha_1, \alpha_2 \in \mathbf{K}$ and $x_1, x_2 \in X$. Since topologies are present, it is the *continuous* linear transformations that deserve our interest.

THEOREM 1.4 A linear transformation $T: X \to Y$ is continuous if and only if it is continuous at 0. The same is true for a seminorm $\rho: X \to \mathbf{R}$.

□ **PROOF** Let T be continuous at 0 and let x in X and any neighborhood $y + U$ of $y = Tx$ be given. By continuity at 0 there exists a neighborhood V of 0 such that $T(V) \subseteq U$ and hence $T(x + V) = Tx + T(V) \subseteq y + U$, so T is continuous at x. Clearly continuity implies continuity at 0. If ρ is continuous at 0, let $x \in X$ and an interval D_ϵ of radius $\epsilon > 0$ about $0 \in \mathbf{R}$ be given. Then there exists a neighborhood V of $0 \in X$, such that $\rho(V) \subseteq D_\epsilon$. Using $\rho(x + v) \leq \rho(x) + \rho(v)$ for each $v \in V$, we conclude that $\rho(x + V) \subseteq \rho(x) + D_\epsilon$ and ρ is continuous at x.

THEOREM 1.5 Let X be a tls over $\mathbf{K}$. Then every linear transformation $T: \mathbf{K}^n \to X$ is continuous.

□ **PROOF**   Since T is linear, it transforms as follows: There exist $x_1, x_2, \ldots, x_n \in X$ such that for any $(\alpha_1, \ldots, \alpha_n) \in \mathbf{K}^n$, $T(\alpha_1, \ldots, \alpha_n) = \sum_{i=1}^{n} \alpha_i x_i$. Indeed $x_i = Te_i$, where $e_i \in \mathbf{K}^n$ has a 1 in the ith component and 0 elsewhere. Let U be any neighborhood of 0 in X and choose by repeated use of Theorem 1.2b a neighborhood V of 0 such that $V + V + \cdots + V \subseteq U$, where the left-hand sum has n terms. For each x_i, $1 \leq i \leq n$, Theorem 1.2c yields a neighborhood $\mathcal{N}_i$ of 0 in $\mathbf{K}$ such that $\mathcal{N}_i x_i \subseteq V$. Then

$$T(\mathcal{N}_1 \times \mathcal{N}_2 \times \cdots \times \mathcal{N}_n) \subseteq V + V + \cdots + V \subseteq U,$$

so T is continuous at 0 and hence continuous.

We define a subset M of a tls X to be *bounded* if for every neighborhood U of 0 there exists $\alpha \in \mathbf{K}$ such that $M \subseteq \alpha U$. This definition is readily seen to be a natural generalization of boundedness in the metric sense, agreeing with the metric definition, for example, when X is a normed linear space. It should also be noted that sets consisting of single points are bounded since neighborhoods of 0 are absorbing.

EXERCISE 1.5   Prove

a. Compact sets in any tls are bounded.
b. If $T: X \to Y$ is a continuous linear transformation, then T carries bounded sets onto bounded sets.

One aspect of the study of structure-preserving mappings from an object under investigation to another object of the same category is the consideration of the special case arising when the codomain is the simplest nontrivial example of the object under investigation. A *linear functional* on X is a linear transformation from X into $\mathbf{K}$, and an important part of the study of a tls X is the investigation of the collection X^* of all *continuous* linear functionals on X. We call X^* the *conjugate space* of X, and care should be taken to distinguish between this and the nontopological notion of the *dual space* of X, the collection of *all* linear functionals on X. The conjugate space X^* is itself a linear space over $\mathbf{K}$ that can (frequently) be topologized by various natural topologies to become a tls. A key result in the study of continuous linear functionals on certain topological linear spaces is the Hahn–Banach theorem, the proof of which depends upon the following ideas.

□ ZORN'S LEMMA AND
THE HAHN–BANACH THEOREM

LEMMA 1.6 Let X be a *complex* linear space, f a linear functional on X, and $h = \operatorname{Re}(f)$. Then

a. h is a real linear functional on $X_{\mathbf{R}}$, the set X taken as a linear space over $\mathbf{R}$ instead of $\mathbf{C}$.
b. h determines f on X by the relation $f(x) = h(x) - ih(ix)$.
c. If ρ is a seminorm on X,

$$\sup_{\rho(x) \leq 1} |f(x)| = \sup_{\rho(x) \leq 1} |h(x)|.$$

d. If ρ is a seminorm and k a linear functional on X, then

$$\sup_{\rho(x) \leq 1} |k(x)| \leq 1 \Longleftrightarrow |k(x)| \leq \rho(x) \qquad \text{for all} \quad x \in X.$$

EXERCISE 1.6 Prove Lemma 1.6.

A *partially ordered set* (poset) $(E; \leq)$ is a nonempty set E together with a relation $\leq$ on E such that

(a) $a \leq a$ for all $a \in E$
(b) $a \leq b$ and $b \leq a \Longrightarrow a = b$
(c) $a \leq b$ and $b \leq c \Longrightarrow a \leq c$.

If $(E; \leq)$ is a poset we make the following definitions:
We call $m \in E$ a *maximal element* for E if $m \leq x \Longrightarrow m = x$ (thus whenever m is related to a given $x \in E$, it must be the case that $x \leq m$).

A subset F of E is *totally ordered* if for every $a, b \in F$, $a \leq b$ or $b \leq a$; and $u \in E$ is an *upper bound* for F if $x \leq u$ for all $x \in F$.

The fundamental result needed is known as Zorn's lemma. It (along with an astonishing number of other fundamental mathematical results) is equivalent to an exceedingly plausible set theoretic procedure known as the axiom of choice, though neither implication will be proved here. (See the Remarks at the end of this chapter.)

LEMMA 1.7 Zorn's Lemma
If every totally ordered subset of a poset E has an upper bound, then E has a maximal element.

EXERCISE 1.7   a. Let V be any vector space and L the collection of all linearly independent subsets of V. Show that if L is ordered by inclusion ($A \leq B$ means $A \subseteq B$), then $(L; \subseteq)$ becomes a poset.

b. Show that $(L; \subseteq)$ satisfies the hypothesis of Zorn's lemma.

c. Conclude that every vector space has a (certainly not unique) maximal linearly independent subset, i.e., a basis.

THEOREM 1.8   **Hahn–Banach Theorem**

Let X be a linear space and ρ a seminorm on X. Let Y be a subspace of X and g a linear functional on Y such that $|g(y)| \leq \rho(y)$ for all $y \in Y$. Then there exists a linear functional f on X such that

(a) $f|_Y = g$ ($f|_Y$ means f restricted to Y).
(b) $|f(x)| \leq \rho(x)$ for all $x \in X$.

□   **PROOF**   By Lemma 1.6 it suffices to consider the case when X is a *real* linear space. Indeed if X is complex and we satisfactorily extend $\operatorname{Re}(g)$ to h on $X_{\mathbf{R}}$, then (b) of the lemma shows how to obtain f, and using (c) and (d): $|h(x)| \leq \rho(x)$ for all $x \Rightarrow \sup_{\rho(x) \leq 1} |h(x)| \leq 1 \Rightarrow \sup_{\rho(x) \leq 1} |f(x)| \leq 1 \Rightarrow |f(x)| \leq \rho(x)$ for all x. Working on the real case then, the set E of all extensions of g to linear functionals f_Z on subspaces $Z \supseteq Y$ that are dominated by ρ on Z ($|f_Z(z)| \leq \rho(z)$) is a nonempty set ($g \in E$). Thus E is a poset under the relation: $f_{Z_1} \leq f_{Z_2}$ if $Z_1 \subseteq Z_2$ and f_{Z_2} agrees with f_{Z_1} on Z_1. If F is a totally ordered subset of E, define $W = \bigcup_{f_Z \in F} Z$ and define f_W on W as follows: Given $w \in W$, choose a subspace Z with $f_Z \in F$ and $w \in Z$, and let $f_W(w) = f_Z(w)$. Then f_W is a well-defined linear functional on W and f_W is an upper bound for F. (Of course it should be checked that f_W is dominated by ρ on W.) Applying the lemma of Zorn, we conclude that E has a maximal element, which we call f_M. We now show that $M = X$ which, upon setting $f_M = f$, will complete the proof. Suppose, on the contrary, that $M \neq X$ and choose any $x \notin M$. We shall extend f_M to $f_N \in E$ where f_N is defined and dominated by ρ on the subspace $N = \{m + \alpha x : m \in M, \alpha \in \mathbf{R}\}$. This will contradict the maximality of f_M, showing $M = X$ and completing the proof. The only problem is to show that f_N can be defined so as to be dominated on N by ρ. This can be done if we define f_N so that for all $m \in M$ and $\alpha \in \mathbf{R}$, $|f_N(m + \alpha x)| = |f_N(m) + \alpha f_N(x)| = |f_M(m) + $

$\alpha f_N(x) \mid \leq \rho(m + \alpha x)$. However,

$$
\begin{aligned}
\mid f_M(m) &+ \alpha f_N(x) \mid \leq \rho(m + \alpha x) \\
&\Leftrightarrow \mid f_M((1/\alpha)m) + f_N(x) \mid \leq \rho((1/\alpha)m + x) \qquad (\alpha \neq 0) \\
&\Leftrightarrow \mid f_M(m) + f_N(x) \mid \leq \rho(m + x) \\
&\Leftrightarrow -\rho(m + x) \leq f_M(m) + f_N(x) \leq \rho(m + x) \\
&\Leftrightarrow -f_M(m) - \rho(m + x) \leq f_N(x) \leq -f_M(m) + \rho(m + x).
\end{aligned}
$$

Let m_1 and m_2 be any members of M. Then

$$
\begin{aligned}
-f_M(m_1) &- \rho(m_1 + x) \\
&= -f_M(m_2) + f_M(m_2) - f_M(m_1) - \rho(m_1 + x) \\
&= -f_M(m_2) + f_M(m_2 - m_1) - \rho(m_1 + x) \\
&\leq -f_M(m_2) + \rho(m_2 - m_1) - \rho(m_1 + x) \\
&\leq -f_M(m_2) + \rho(m_2 + x) + \rho(-(m_1 + x)) - \rho(m_1 + x) \\
&= -f_M(m_2) + \rho(m_2 + x).
\end{aligned}
$$

This shows that the interval

$$
[\sup_{m \in M} \{-f_M(m) - \rho(m + x)\}, \quad \inf_{m \in M} \{-f_M(m) + \rho(m + x)\}]
$$

is nonempty, and hence defining $f_N(x)$ to be any value in this non-empty interval and using the above chain of equivalences, we have established our contradiction and proved the theorem.

As an elementary but representative application of this theorem, consider

EXERCISE 1.8   Let X be a tls, ρ a continuous seminorm on X, and $x_0 \in X$. Prove that there exists a linear functional f on X such that

(a) $f(x_0) = \rho(x_0)$, and
(b) $\mid f(x) \mid \leq \rho(x)$ for all $x \in X$ and hence f is continuous on X.

Hints: Choose the subspace Y of X to be one (or conceivably even zero) dimensional. Use the continuity of ρ at 0 to deduce continuity of f at 0.

It is readily seen that for every seminorm ρ on a linear space X the set $\{x \in X : \rho(x) \leq 1\}$ is an absorbing, balanced, convex subset of X. It is of fundamental importance to the study of locally convex topological linear spaces that, conversely, any absorbing, balanced, convex subset U of X determines a seminorm on X. Given such a set U, define the *gauge* ρ of U by

$$\rho(x) = \inf\{r > 0 : x \in rU\}.$$

EXERCISE 1.9   a. Given a seminorm ρ, prove $\{x \in X : \rho(x) \le 1\}$ is absorbing, balanced, and convex.
   b. Given absorbing, balanced, convex sets U and V with gauges ρ_U and ρ_V, show $U \subseteq V \Longrightarrow \rho_V \le \rho_U$.
   c. Given U as above with gauge ρ, prove

   $$\{x \in X : \rho(x) < 1\} \subseteq U \subseteq \{x \in X : \rho(x) \le 1\}.$$

THEOREM 1.9   If U is an absorbing, balanced, convex subset of a linear space X, then the gauge ρ of U is a seminorm on X. If X is a tls and U is a balanced, convex neighborhood of 0, then ρ is a *continuous* seminorm on X.

□   **PROOF**   The absorbing property of U (or in the neighborhood of 0 case, Theorem 1.2c) ensures that ρ is finitely defined for each $x \in X$. If $t > 0$,

$$
\begin{aligned}
t\rho(x) &= t \cdot \inf\{s > 0 : x \in sU\} \\
&= \inf\{ts > 0 : x \in sU\} \\
&= \inf\{r > 0 : x \in (r/t)U\} \qquad (\text{let } r = st) \\
&= \inf\{r > 0 : tx \in rU\} = \rho(tx).
\end{aligned}
$$

If $\alpha \in \mathbf{K}, |\alpha| = 1$, we have

$$
\begin{aligned}
\rho(\alpha x) &= \inf\{r > 0 : \alpha x \in rU\} \\
&= \inf\{r > 0 : x \in rU\} \qquad (\text{since } rU \text{ is balanced}) \\
&= \rho(x) = |\alpha|\rho(x).
\end{aligned}
$$

Combining the results for $t > 0$ and $|\alpha| = 1$ gives $\rho(\beta x) = |\beta|\rho(x)$ for all $\beta \in \mathbf{K}$. For the triangle inequality, let $x, y \in X$ and $\epsilon > 0$ be given and choose $r, s > 0$ such that

$$\rho(x) \le r < \rho(x) + \epsilon/2 \qquad (x \in rU)$$

and

$$\rho(y) \le s < \rho(y) + \epsilon/2 \qquad (y \in sU).$$

This is possible by the definition of ρ. Then there exist $u_1, u_2 \in U$ such that $x = ru_1$ and $y = su_2$. Choosing $c = r/(r + s)$, we then have $x + y = ru_1 + su_2 = (r + s)(cu_1 + (1 - c)u_2) \in (r + s)U$ by convexity of U. Hence $\rho(x + y) \le r + s < \rho(x) + \rho(y) + \epsilon$, and since $\epsilon > 0$ was arbitrary, $\rho(x + y) \le \rho(x) + \rho(y)$. To prove that ρ is continuous when X is a tls and U is a neighborhood of 0, note that $\rho(u) \le 1$ for all $u \in U$. Thus for any $\epsilon > 0$, $\rho(u) \le \epsilon$ for all $u \in \epsilon U$, so ρ is continuous at 0 and hence by Theorem 1.4, ρ is continuous.

The three important ideas most recently under discussion are all neatly connected by

THEOREM 1.10   Let X be a tls. The following are equivalent.

    a. There exists a proper convex neighborhood of 0 (proper means $\ne X$).

    b. There exists a nonzero continuous seminorm on X.

    c. There exists a nonzero continuous linear functional on X.

□   **PROOF**   (a) ⟹ (b): By Theorem 1.3i every convex neighborhood of 0 contains a balanced convex subneighborhood, whence Theorem 1.9 applies.

(b) ⟹ (c): If ρ is the nonzero continuous seminorm, choose $x_0 \in X$ such that $\rho(x_0) \ne 0$. An application of Exercise 1.8 yields a linear functional that is nonzero since $f(x_0) = \rho(x_0)$, and continuous since $|f(x)| \le \rho(x)$.

(c) ⟹ (a): If f is a nonzero continuous linear functional on X, define $U = \{x \in X : |f(x)| \le 1\}$. Then U is clearly a proper neighborhood of 0; and if $u, v \in U$, we have

$$|f(tu + (1 - t)v)| = |tf(u) + (1 - t)f(v)| \le t + (1 - t) = 1,$$

so U is convex.

Having established the connection between convex neighborhoods of 0 and continuous linear functionals, we specialize our study of topological linear spaces in Chapter 2 to those that have an "ample" supply of convex neighborhoods of 0, the *locally convex* topological linear spaces.

☐ REMARKS

As might be expected from the theory of vector spaces, there are standard ways of building up new topological linear spaces from old ones. Specifically, a subspace M of a tls X determines a quotient tls X/M which is Hausdorff if and only if M is closed in X. Similarly, a product of topological linear spaces is a tls under the usual product topology. These results present no surprises and we will not need them until we discuss more specialized spaces, where more direct arguments are available.

While a feel for some of the geometric concepts introduced on a tls can be obtained by using $\mathbf{R}^2$ as a model (see Problem 1 following), this procedure is not always adequate. As Problem 2 shows, certain infinite-dimensional spaces have the property that none of their neighborhoods of 0 are bounded. A related result is that a Hausdorff tls is locally compact (i.e., has a compact neighborhood of 0) if and only if it is finite dimensional. See Kelley and Namioka's book [2, p. 62] for a proof of this result.

Problem 5 (which uses Problems 3 and 4) shows in particular that every n-dimensional normed linear space is homeomorphic to $\mathbf{K}^n$. By using nets instead of sequences (or more elaborate arguments) this result can be extended to a Hausdorff tls. Thus the real substance of the theory of topological linear spaces and of functional analysis in general lies in infinite-dimensional spaces.

There are examples of Hausdorff topological linear spaces that have no nonzero continuous linear functionals (see Chapter 2, Problem 2). In view of the above remarks and Theorem 1.5 these spaces must be infinite dimensional. We shall also find it quite easy after Chapter 2 to construct infinite-dimensional spaces all of whose linear functionals are continuous (see Chapter 2, Problem 3).

The axiom of choice says that given any collection $\{S_\alpha\}_{\alpha \in I}$ of nonempty sets, there exists a choice function γ that singles out some one element $s_\alpha = \gamma(S_\alpha)$ from each set S_α. More concisely, but perhaps less formally, this says that the Cartesian product of any nonempty collection of nonempty sets is nonempty. While one is always reluctant to add additional axioms to those already present in set theory, many fundamental results of mathematics appear to depend upon the axiom of choice. Furthermore, it has been shown that if use of the axiom of choice leads to an inconsistency in mathematics, then an inconsistency is already present without the axiom. For a development of the axiom of choice, Zorn's lemma, and their equivalence see Zaanen's book [3, p. 4].

The Hahn–Banach theorem will be an invaluable tool for generating continuous linear functionals with desired properties (cf. Exercise 1.8). Another fruitful source of continuous linear functionals are the "separation theorems," which we do not consider here. (See Wilansky's book [4, p. 219].)

□ **PROBLEMS**

1. a. Letting

$$A = \{(x,y) \in \mathbf{R}^2 : y = 1/x, x < 0\} \quad \text{and}$$
$$B = \{(x,y) \in \mathbf{R}^2 : x = 0, y \geq 0\},$$

   show that the inclusion in Theorem 1.3c cannot be replaced by an equality. This will also show that *closed* cannot replace *compact* in (d) of that theorem.
   b. By working in $\mathbf{R}^2$ show that the convex hull of a closed set need not be closed.

2. Show that the space $\mathbf{\mathcal{C}}(D)$ of Example 1 has no bounded neighborhood of 0. Hint: Let $\bar{D}_r$ be the closed disk about 0 of radius r, let

$$U_{\bar{D}_r,\epsilon} = \{f \in \mathbf{\mathcal{C}}(D) : |f(z)| < \epsilon \text{ for all } z \in \bar{D}_r\},$$

   and look at the functions $f_k \in U_{\bar{D}_r,\epsilon}$ defined by

$$f_k(z) = \epsilon(z/r)^k \quad (k = 1, 2, \ldots).$$

3. Let f be a linear functional on a tls X. Prove that f is continuous $\Leftrightarrow \ker(f) = \{x \in X : f(x) = 0\}$ is closed. Hints for the nontrivial implication:
   i. Assume $f \neq 0$ and find $x \in X$ and a balanced neighborhood U of 0 in X such that $(x - U) \cap \ker(f) = \emptyset$.
   ii. Show $f(x) \notin f(U)$ and that $f(U)$ is balanced in $\mathbf{K}$.
   iii. Show $f(U) \subseteq \{\alpha \in \mathbf{K} : |\alpha| \leq \mathcal{N}\}$ for some $\mathcal{N} > 0$.

4. A sequence $\{x_n\}$ in a tls X is defined to be *Cauchy* if for every neighborhood U of 0 in X there exists $\mathcal{N}$ such that $m, n > \mathcal{N} \Rightarrow$

$x_m - x_n \in U$. If every Cauchy sequence in X is convergent, X is said to be *sequentially complete*.

a. Show that if the topology on X is determined by a *translation invariant metric* $(d(x + w, y + w) = d(x, y))$, then the above notion of completeness coincides with completeness in a metric space. Note that norms induce translation invariant metrics.

b. Prove that if $T : X \to Y$ is a *linear* homeomorphism between topological linear spaces, then T preserves Cauchy sequences, and Y is sequentially complete if and only if X is.

c. Let X be a normed linear space (or any tls with a countable neighborhood base at 0). Prove that a (sequentially) complete subspace of X is closed in X.

5. Let X be a Hausdorff tls with a countable neighborhood base at 0. Prove that every n-dimensional subspace F of X is complete, closed in X, and homeomorphic to $\mathbf{K}^n$ via a linear mapping. Hints: Choose a basis $x_1, x_2, \ldots, x_n$ for F and define $T : \mathbf{K}^n \to F$ by

$$T(\alpha_1, \ldots, \alpha_n) = \sum_{i=1}^{n} \alpha_i x_i.$$

   i. Argue that T is a continuous bijection. Using Problem 3 (twice), Problem 4, and induction on n show:

   ii. When $n = 1$, T is a homeomorphism and hence F is complete and closed in X.

   iii. Assuming this result holds for $n - 1$, let $\dim(F) = n$ and prove that with $x = \sum_{i=1}^{n} \alpha_i(x) x_i$,

$$T^{-1} : F \to \mathbf{K}^n, \qquad T^{-1}(x) = (\alpha_1(x), \ldots, \alpha_n(x))$$

   is continuous. What is the dimension of $\ker(\alpha_i)$ for each i?

6. Let X be a tls containing an infinite subset $\{x_n\}_{n=1}^{\infty}$ that is both linearly independent and bounded. Prove that there exists a discontinuous linear functional on X. Hint: Define $f : X \to \mathbf{K}$ so that $f(x_n) = n$.

Locally Convex Spaces

2

□ **CHARACTERIZATION AND EXAMPLES**

At the end of Chapter 1 the value of a tls having lots of convex neighborhoods of 0 was pointed out. Thus the following definitions are fairly natural ones.

A tls is called *locally convex* if it has a neighborhood base at 0 consisting of convex sets. A *locally convex space* is a locally convex tls that is Hausdorff.

We first prove a characterization theorem for locally convex spaces similar to Theorem 1.2.

THEOREM 2.1   Let X be a locally convex space. Then there exists a neighborhood base $\mathfrak{F}$ at 0 such that

(a) $U, V \in \mathfrak{F} \implies U \cap V \in \mathfrak{F}$.
(b) $U \in \mathfrak{F}$ and $\alpha \neq 0 \implies \alpha U \in \mathfrak{F}$.
(c) $U \in \mathfrak{F} \implies U$ is absorbing.
(d) $U \in \mathfrak{F} \implies U$ is balanced and convex.
(e) $\bigcap_{U \in \mathfrak{F}} U = \{0\}$.

Conversely, if X is a linear space and $\mathfrak{F}$ a family of subsets of X satisfying (a)–(e), then there exists a topology on X with respect to which X is a locally convex space and $\mathfrak{F}$ a neighborhood at 0.

□   **PROOF**   If X is a locally convex space, define $\mathfrak{F}$ to be the family of all balanced convex neighborhoods of 0 in X. By Theorem 1.3i, $\mathfrak{F}$ is a neighborhood base at 0. Properties (a) and (b) hold by Exercise 1.1. Properties (c) and (d) follow from corresponding results of Theorem 1.2. The "conversely" part has essentially been established in Theorem 1.2. To make this claim precise we need only show that conditions (a)–(d) of Theorem 2.1 imply (a)–(d) of Theorem 1.2. Since U is convex, in (b) we have $\frac{1}{2}U + \frac{1}{2}U \subseteq U$ (in fact equality holds) yielding (b) of Theorem 1.2 (choose $V = \frac{1}{2}U$). Condition (d) of Theorem 1.2 results from (b) of Theorem 2.1 and the fact that $U \in \mathfrak{F} \implies U$ is balanced (choose $V = (1/r)U$). Condition (e) ensures that the locally convex topology obtained will be Hausdorff.

As indicated in Example 1 of Chapter 1, we will be considering topologies on X generated by sets $\mathcal{P} = \{\rho_\alpha\}_{\alpha \in A}$ of seminorms on X. A set $\mathcal{P}$ of seminorms is called *total* if $\rho(x) = 0$ for all $\rho \in \mathcal{P} \Rightarrow x = 0$.

The following exercise should recall for the reader a fundamental property of analytic functions, a property which is not shared by those that are merely continuous.

EXERCISE 2.1   a. With $\mathcal{Q}(D)$ and ρ_K as in Example 1, Chapter 1, prove that if K has nonempty interior, the singleton set $\{\rho_K\}$ is by itself total, i.e., ρ_K is a norm.

b. Let $\mathcal{C}(D)$ be the continuous (real- or complex-) valued functions on D and for each compact K contained in D define ρ_K as in Example 1, but with $\mathcal{C}(D)$ as its domain. Letting $\mathcal{P}$ be the set of all such ρ_K, prove that $\mathcal{P}$ is total, but that no finite subset of $\mathcal{P}$ is total. Precisely which subsets of $\mathcal{P}$ are total?

THEOREM 2.2   Let X be a locally convex space and let $\mathcal{P}$ be the family of all continuous seminorms on X.

a. The family of (open) unit balls

$$\{x \in X : \rho(x) < 1\} \qquad (\rho \in \mathcal{P})$$

is a neighborhood base at 0 for X.
b. $\mathcal{P}$ is total.

□   **PROOF**

(a) Given any neighborhood V of 0, obtain (Theorem 2.1) a convex balanced subneighborhood U of 0. Let ρ be the gauge of U. By Theorem 1.9, $\rho \in \mathcal{P}$; and by the definition of ρ,

$$\{x \in X : \rho(x) < 1\} \subseteq U \subseteq V,$$

so the unit balls do form a neighborhood base at 0.
(b) $\rho(y) = 0$ for all $\rho \in \mathcal{P} \Rightarrow y \in \bigcap_{\rho \in \mathcal{P}}\{x \in X : \rho(x) < 1\} \Rightarrow y = 0$ by (a) above and Theorem 2.1e.

The definition of a locally convex space is given in terms of a neighborhood base at 0 (of convex sets), while Example 1 of Chapter 1 is presented by means of the weakest topology generated by a (necessarily total) set of seminorms. By applying the "conversely" part of Theorem 2.1 to the collection $\mathcal{F}$ of neighborhoods

$$U_{i_1, \epsilon_1, i_2, \epsilon_2, \ldots, i_n, \epsilon_n}$$

$$= \{x \in X : \rho_{i_k}(x) < \epsilon_k, \quad k = 1, 2, \ldots, n\} \quad (\rho_{i_k} \in \mathcal{P}, \epsilon_k > 0)$$

it is readily seen that this weakest topology does indeed make X a locally convex space. Theorem 2.2 says that Example 1 (with $\mathcal{P}$ total) is the "only" example of a locally convex space; i.e., every locally convex space can be viewed as arising in this way. This certainly does not preclude us from looking at specific examples of this process, and indeed $\mathcal{C}(D)$ is one such. To set the stage for the definition of a distribution space we now consider another specific example of a locally convex space.

Let K be a compact subset of $\mathbf{R}^n$ and consider the linear space $\mathcal{C}_K^\infty(\mathbf{R}^n)$ of infinitely differentiable real- or complex-valued functions on $\mathbf{R}^n$ that vanish outside of K. For each n-tuple $s = (s_1, s_2, \ldots, s_n)$ of nonnegative integers, let $|s| = s_1 + \cdots + s_n$, and for each such s define the (partial) differential operator

$$D^s = \partial^{|s|} / \partial x_1^{s_1} \partial x_2^{s_2} \ldots \partial x_n^{s_n}$$

(i.e., s_1 partials with respect to $x_1, \ldots, s_n$ partials with respect to x_n). For each nonnegative integer m, define a seminorm $\rho_{K,m}$ on $\mathcal{C}_K^\infty(\mathbf{R}^n)$ by

$$\rho_{K,m}(f) = \sup_{\substack{|s| \le m \\ x \in K}} |D^s f(x)|.$$

We denote by $\mathfrak{D}_K(\mathbf{R}^n)$ the locally convex space obtained by giving $\mathcal{C}_K^\infty(\mathbf{R}^n)$ the weakest topology such that all the $\rho_{K,m}$ are continuous. It is readily seen that $f_n \to 0$ in $\mathfrak{D}_K(\mathbf{R}^n)$ if and only if, for every s, $D^s f_n \to 0$ uniformly on K (and hence on $\mathbf{R}^n$). Note that so far in this example the compact set K has been fixed. We shall return to and elaborate upon this example later in this chapter.

□   **CONTINUOUS LINEAR TRANSFORMATIONS
AND FUNCTIONALS**

We have seen that a locally convex space can be defined in terms of a collection of seminorms or in terms of a neighborhood base at 0 of convex sets. It should be no surprise that the continuity of a linear transformation between locally convex spaces has a natural characterization in terms of seminorms.

THEOREM 2.3   Let X and Y be locally convex spaces whose topologies are generated, respectively, by collections $\mathcal{P}$ and Σ of seminorms. Then a linear transformation $T : X \rightarrow Y$ is continuous $\Longleftrightarrow$ for every $\sigma \in \Sigma$ there exists a continuous seminorm ρ on X such that $\sigma(Tx) \leq \rho(x)$ for every $x \in X$.

□   **PROOF**
$\Longrightarrow$: Let $\sigma \in \Sigma$ be given and define $V = \{y \in Y : \sigma(y) < 1\}$. Then T continuous $\Longrightarrow T$ continuous at $0 \Longrightarrow$ there exists a balanced convex neighborhood U of X such that $T(U) \subseteq V$. Let ρ be the gauge of U; it will be shown that $\sigma(Tx) \leq \rho(x)$ for all $x \in X$. Suppose on the contrary that $\sigma(Tx) > \rho(x)$ for some $x \in X$. Letting $y = T(x/\sigma(Tx))$, we have $\sigma(y) = \sigma(Tx)/\sigma(Tx) = 1 \Longrightarrow y \notin V$. But

$$\rho(x/\sigma(Tx)) = \rho(x)/\sigma(Tx) < 1 \Longrightarrow x/\sigma(Tx) \in U \Longrightarrow y \in T(U).$$

This contradicts $T(U) \subseteq V$ and establishes the result.
$\Longleftarrow$: The sets $V = \{y \in Y : \sigma(y) < 1\}$, $\sigma \in \Sigma$, form a neighborhood subbase of 0 in Y, and it suffices to show that for any such V there exists a neighborhood U of 0 in X such that $T(U) \subseteq V$. Given such a V, arising from $\sigma \in \Sigma$, let ρ be a continuous seminorm on X such that $\sigma(Tx) \leq \rho(x)$. Let $U = \{x \in X : \rho(x) < 1\}$. Then $y \in T(U) \Longrightarrow y = Tx$ with $\rho(x) < 1 \Longrightarrow \sigma(y) = \sigma(Tx) \leq \rho(x) < 1 \Longrightarrow y \in V$. This shows that $T(U) \subseteq V$ and completes the proof.

If in Theorem 2.3, Y is replaced by the scalar field **K**, whose topology is generated by the single norm $| \ |$, we obtain a useful characterization for continuity of linear functionals. Likewise if both X and Y are normed linear spaces (topologies generated by a single norm), the condition of the theorem is considerably simplified and will be useful (and proved in another way) in Chapter 3. Specifically, we have

COROLLARY   a. Let X be a locally convex space. Then a linear functional $f: X \to \mathbf{K}$ is continuous if and only if there exists a continuous seminorm ρ on X such that $|f(x)| \le \rho(x)$ for all $x \in X$.

b. Let $(X, \|\ \|_1)$ and $(Y, \|\ \|_2)$ be normed linear spaces. Then a linear transformation $T: X \to Y$ is continuous if and only if for some $C \ge 0, \|Tx\|_2 \le C\|x\|_1$ for all $x \in X$.

EXERCISE 2.2   Let X be a tls and Y a locally convex space. Prove that a linear transformation $T: X \to Y$ is continuous if and only if $\rho \circ T$ is continuous for every continuous seminorm ρ on Y.

LEMMA 2.4   a. A linear functional f or a seminorm ρ on a tls X is continuous $\iff$ it is bounded on some neighborhood of 0 in X.

b. The kernel of a nonzero linear functional f on a linear space X has *codimension* 1, i.e., $\ker(f) \ne X$, and for any $x_0 \notin \ker(f)$, $\text{span}(\ker(f) \cup \{x_0\}) = X$.

c. Let $f_1, f_2, \ldots, f_n$ be linear functionals on a linear space X. Then a linear functional f is a linear combination of $f_1, f_2, \ldots, f_n \iff \bigcap_{i=1}^{n} \ker(f_i) \subseteq \ker(f)$.

□   **PROOF**

(a) $\implies$: If f is continuous, then $U = \{x \in X : |f(x)| \le 1\}$ is a neighborhood of 0 on which f is certainly bounded.

$\impliedby$: If f is bounded on some neighborhood U of 0, then there exists $N > 0$ such that $|f(x)| < N$ for all $x \in U$. Given $\epsilon > 0$ it follows that $|f(x)| < \epsilon$ for all $x \in (\epsilon/N)U$, so f is continuous at 0 and hence continuous. The seminorm proofs are identical.

(b) Consider any $x_0 \in X$ with $x_0 \notin \ker(f)$. Given any $x \in X$, let $\alpha = f(x)/f(x_0)$. Then $x = (x - \alpha x_0) + \alpha x_0$ and $f(x - \alpha x_0) = f(x) - \alpha f(x_0) = 0$. This shows that $x - \alpha x_0 \in \ker(f)$ and hence that $x \in \text{span}(\ker(f) \cup \{x_0\})$, completing (b).

(c) $\implies$: This follows directly from the definitions of linear combination and kernel.

$\Leftarrow$: We proceed by induction on n. When $n = 1$, the condition $\ker(f_1) \subseteq \ker(f)$ yields, using (b), either $\ker(f) = X$ or the existence of $x_0 \in \ker(f)$ and $\ker(f_1) = \ker(f)$. In the former case $f = 0$, so f is certainly a linear combination of f_1. In the latter case let $\alpha = f(x_0)/f_1(x_0)$ and observe that $f - \alpha f_1$ is zero on span $\{x_0\}$. By (b) $f - \alpha f_1$ is zero on all of X and we conclude that $f = \alpha f_1$. Assuming the result for a general n, suppose we have linear functionals $f_1, f_2, \ldots, f_{n+1}$ and f such that $\bigcap_{i=1}^{n+1} \ker(f_i) \subseteq \ker(f)$. If $\bigcap_{i=1}^{n} \ker(f_i) \subseteq \ker(f)$, then we are done; otherwise choose $x_0 \in X$ with $x_0 \in \bigcap_{i=1}^{n} \ker(f_i)$ and $f(x_0) \neq 0$. Then $f_{n+1}(x_0) \neq 0$ (why?) and we may define a linear functional $g = f - \alpha f_{n+1}$ where $\alpha = f(x_0)/f_{n+1}(x_0)$, and we claim that

$$\bigcap_{i=1}^{n} \ker(f_i) \subseteq \ker(g). \tag{1}$$

To show this let h be the restriction of g to the linear space $Y = \bigcap_{i=1}^{n} \ker(f_i)$. Since $g = f - \alpha f_{n+i}$ and $\bigcap_{i=1}^{n+1} \ker(f_i) \subseteq \ker(f)$ we have $\ker(f_{n+1}|_Y) \subseteq \ker(g|_Y) = \ker(h)$. The x_0 chosen above shows that the inclusion is proper ($f_{n+1}(x_0) \neq 0$, but $g(x_0) = 0$) and (b) then shows that $\ker(h) = Y$, i.e. $h = 0$. This is simply a disguised form of (1). The induction hypothesis applied to (1) gives that g is a linear combination of $f_1, f_2, \ldots, f_n$ and hence that f is a linear combination of $f_1, f_2, \ldots, f_{n+1}$. This completes the proof.

It is readily checked that the modulus of a linear functional f is a seminorm. Furthermore, f continuous $\Leftrightarrow f$ continuous at $0 \Leftrightarrow |f|$ continuous at $0 \Leftrightarrow |f|$ continuous. It follows that a linear space can be topologized by means of a family of linear functionals rather than seminorms. When this is done, the following expected but useful result emerges.

THEOREM 2.5 Let X be a linear space and $\mathfrak{F}$ a family of linear functionals on X which is total. Give X the weakest topology such that every $f \in \mathfrak{F}$ is continuous. Then

a. X is a locally convex space.

b. Every continuous linear functional on X is a linear combination of functionals in $\mathfrak{F}$.

☐ **PROOF**

(a) As noted above, for every $f \in \mathfrak{F}$, $|f|$ is a seminorm and f is continuous if and only if $|f|$ is. Hence the weakest topology generated by $\mathfrak{F}$ is identical to that generated by the seminorms $|f|$, $f \in \mathfrak{F}$; and we established earlier in this chapter that this makes X a locally convex space. Note that a neighborhood base at 0 in X consists of sets of the form

$$U = \{x \in X : |f_i(x)| < \epsilon, i = 1, 2, \ldots, n\} \qquad (f_i \in \mathfrak{F}, \ \epsilon > 0).$$

(b) If f is a continuous linear functional on X, then by Lemma 2.4a, f is bounded on some neighborhood of 0 in X. Hence there exist $f_1, \ldots, f_n \in \mathfrak{F}$, $\epsilon > 0$, and $N > 0$ such that $|f_i(x)| < \epsilon$ for $i = 1, \ldots, n \Rightarrow |f(x)| \leq N$. Then

$$x \in \bigcap_{i=1}^{n} \ker(f_i) \Rightarrow f_i(x) = 0 \qquad \text{for} \quad i = 1, \ldots, n$$

$$\Rightarrow f_i(kx) = 0 \qquad \text{for} \quad i = 1, \ldots, n$$
$$\text{and} \quad k = 1, 2 \ldots$$
$$\Rightarrow |f(kx)| \leq N \qquad \text{for} \quad k = 1, 2, \ldots$$
$$\Rightarrow |f(x)| \leq N/k \qquad \text{for} \quad k = 1, 2, \ldots$$
$$\Rightarrow |f(x)| = 0 \Rightarrow x \in \ker(f).$$

An application of Lemma 2.4c then shows that f is a linear combination of $f_1, \ldots, f_n$, completing the proof.

If X is a tls and M is a (linear) subspace of X, we observe that M with its subspace topology is also a tls. A similar result holds in the case of a locally convex space. We can thus speak of the *continuous* linear functionals on the subspace M. We then have the following consequences of the Hahn–Banach theorem.

THEOREM 2.6 Let M be a subspace of a locally convex space X.

a. Any continuous linear functional on M can be extended to a continuous linear functional on X.

b. If M is closed and $x \notin M$, then there exists a continuous linear functional f on X such that $f|_M = 0$ and $f(x) \neq 0$.

□ **PROOF**

(a) If g is a continuous linear functional on M, then by Lemma 2.4a, g is bounded on some neighborhood of 0 in M. It is no loss of generality to assume that g is bounded by 1 on such a neighborhood, from which it follows by the definition of the relative topology that there exists a neighborhood V of 0 in X such that $|g(x)| \leq 1$ for all x in $V \cap M$. Let U be a balanced, convex subneighborhood of V in X and let ρ be the continuous seminorm on X which is the gauge of U. Then $|g(x)| \leq 1$ whenever $x \in U \cap M$, so that

$$\sup_{\substack{\rho(x) \leq 1 \\ x \in M}} |g(x)| \leq 1.$$

It then follows by Lemma 1.6d that $|g(x)| \leq \rho(x)$ for all $x \in M$. An application of the Hahn–Banach theorem now yields a linear functional f on X with $f|_M = g$ and $|f(x)| \leq \rho(x)$ for all $x \in X$. Since ρ is continuous, so is f.

(b) Since M is closed and $x \notin M$, we can choose a balanced neighborhood U of 0 in X such that $(x + U) \cap M = \emptyset$. Let

$$\mathcal{N} = \{m + \alpha x : m \in M, \alpha \in \mathbf{K}\}$$

and define a linear functional g on the subspace $\mathcal{N}$ by $g(m + \alpha x) = \alpha$ (note that g is well defined since $x \notin M$). Then $g|_M = 0$ and $g(x) = 1$. We will show that g is bounded on $U \cap \mathcal{N}$, from which it will follow that g is continuous on $\mathcal{N}$. An application of (a) will then yield a continuous extension of g which will be the desired linear functional on X. Accordingly, let $y \in U \cap \mathcal{N}$, so $y = m + \alpha x \in U$. It follows that either $\alpha = 0$ (whence $g(y) = 0$) or $\alpha^{-1}m + x \in \alpha^{-1}U$. This shows that $|\alpha| < 1$ since otherwise $|\alpha| \geq 1 \Rightarrow \alpha^{-1}U \subseteq U$ (U is balanced) $\Rightarrow x - u = \alpha^{-1}m$ for some $u \in U$, which contradicts the fact that $(x + U) \cap M = \emptyset$. Thus we have

$$y \in U \cap \mathcal{N} \Rightarrow |g(y)| = |g(m + \alpha x)| = |\alpha| < 1,$$

so g is bounded on $U \cap \mathcal{N}$.

EXERCISE 2.3   Prove that the collection X^* of continuous linear functionals on a locally convex space is total, and thereby conclude that X^* *separates points* ($x \neq y \Rightarrow$ there exists $f \in X^*$ such that $f(x) \neq f(y)$).

☐ **TOPOLOGIES ON THE CONJUGATE SPACE $X*$**

Having established various results about the existence of continuous linear functionals on a locally convex space X, we are now prepared to examine possible ways of topologizing the conjugate space $X*$ (all continuous linear functionals on X) so that it too becomes a locally convex space. We start with two definitions that utilize a kind of duality between X and $X*$.

Given $A \subseteq X$, the *annihilator* of A is

$$A^{\perp} = \{f \in X* : f|_A = 0\}.$$

Similarly, for $S \subseteq X*$,

$$S^{\perp} = \{x \in X : f(x) = 0 \text{ for all } f \in S\}.$$

Given $A \subseteq X$, the *polar* of A is

$$A^{\circ} = \{f \in X* : |f(x)| \le 1 \text{ for all } x \in A\},$$

and for $S \subseteq X*$,

$$S^{\circ} = \{x \in X : |f(x)| \le 1 \text{ for all } f \in S\}.$$

EXERCISE 2.4 Given any tls X, verify for $A, B \subseteq X$ and $S \subseteq X*$.

a. $A \subseteq B \Rightarrow B^{\perp} \subseteq A^{\perp}$ and similarly for polars.
b. $S \subseteq S^{\circ\circ}$.
c. $A^{\perp}$ is a subspace of the linear space $X*$ and $S^{\perp}$ is a closed subspace of X.

THEOREM 2.7 Let X be a locally convex space and $A \subseteq X$.

a. The closed subspace generated by A is $(A^{\perp})^{\perp}$.
b. $(A^{\circ})^{\circ}$ is a closed, balanced, convex set containing A, and $A^{\circ} = ((A^{\circ})^{\circ})^{\circ}$ (henceforth parentheses may be dropped).

☐ **PROOF**

(a) $A^{\perp\perp} = \{x \in X : f(x) = 0 \text{ for all } f \in X* \text{ which are } 0 \text{ on } A\}$. Thus $A \subseteq A^{\perp\perp}$ and $A^{\perp\perp}$ is a closed subspace as the intersection of all the closed subspaces $\ker(f)$, $f \in A^{\perp}$. Hence $\overline{\text{span}(A)} \subseteq$

$A^{\perp\perp}$. To show that $\overline{\mathrm{span}\,(A)} = A^{\perp\perp}$, suppose $x \notin \overline{\mathrm{span}\,(A)}$. Then by Theorem 2.6b there exists $f \in X^*$ such that $f\,|\,\overline{\mathrm{span}(A)} = 0$ and $f(x) \neq 0$. Thus $f \in A^\perp$ and $f(x) \neq 0$, so $x \notin A^{\perp\perp}$, completing the proof.

(b) By definition we have

$$A^{\circ\circ} = \{x \in X : |f(x)| \leq 1 \text{ for all } f \in X^* \text{ bounded by 1 on } A\}.$$

Clearly $A \subseteq A^{\circ\circ}$. Also $A^{\circ\circ}$ is closed, balanced, and convex as the intersection of sets of the form

$$\{x \in X : |f(x)| \leq 1\} \qquad (f \in A^\circ).$$

Finally, $A \subseteq A^{\circ\circ} \Longrightarrow A^\circ \supseteq (A^{\circ\circ})^\circ$, while at the same time (using Exercise 2.4b) $S \subseteq S^{\circ\circ}$ with $S = A^\circ$ gives $A^\circ \subseteq (A^{\circ\circ})^\circ$. Thus $A^\circ = (A^{\circ\circ})^\circ$.

If X is a locally convex space, the *weak topology* on X is the weakest topology such that every $f \in X^*$ is continuous. We shall denote X endowed with its weak topology by X_{w}. By Exercise 2.3 and Theorem 2.5, X_{w} is also a locally convex space and every $f \in (X_{\mathrm{w}})^*$ (the *weakly continuous* linear functionals on X) is a member of X^*. Since the weak topology on X is at least as weak as its original topology, it follows that X and X_{w} have precisely the same continuous linear functionals.

EXERCISE 2.5 Prove that a subspace of a locally convex space is closed if and only if it is weakly closed (i.e., closed in the weak topology).

We now consider various ways of topologizing X^*, the conjugate space of a locally convex space X. First, we note that every $x \in X$ determines a linear functional $\hat{x}$ on X^* by the definition

$$\hat{x}(f) = f(x), \qquad f \in X^*.$$

The *weak* topology* on X^* is the weakest topology on X^* such that every $\hat{x}$ $(x \in X)$ is continuous on X^*. We denote X^* with the weak* topology by X_{w}^*. Said in another way, the weak* topology is generated by the seminorms $\rho_x : X^* \to \mathbf{R}$, where

$$\rho_x(f) = f(x) \qquad (x \in X).$$

Thus $f_i \to f$ in X_{w}^* means pointwise convergence (or uniform convergence on finite sets). Note that X_w^* is indeed a locally convex space since the collection $\{\rho_x : x \in X\}$ is total (why?).

The *strong topology* on X^*, denoted by X_s^*, is the topology generated by the family of seminorms

$$\rho_A(f) = \sup_{x \in A} |f(x)|$$

for all bounded subsets A of X ($\rho_A(f)$ is finite by Exercise 1.5b). Note that since points are bounded sets, the strong topology on X^* is at least as strong as the weak* topology.

Not only is every $\hat{x}$ continuous on X_w^*, but by Theorem 2.5b every continuous linear functional is an $\hat{x}$ for some $x \in X$. Hence $(X_w^*)^* = \hat{X}$, where $\hat{X} = \{\hat{x} : x \in X\}$.

In the case of $(X_s^*)^*$ the situation is as follows:

EXERCISE 2.6   Show that the mapping $X \overset{\wedge}{\to} (X_s^*)^*$ ($\hat{x}(f) = f(x)$) is linear and injective. (The above paragraph showed that for $(X_w^*)^*$ the mapping is also surjective and hence an isomorphism.)

If $\wedge$ with codomain $(X_s^*)^*$ is surjective so that $X = (X_s^*)^*$, then X is called *semireflexive*. If in addition the mapping provides a homeomorphism between X and $(X_s^*)_s^*$, then X is called *reflexive*.

The weak* and strong topologies may be viewed in a way that facilitates the introduction on X^* of numerous other topologies which are intermediate in strength. Noticing that a neighborhood base at 0 for the weak* topology can be obtained by taking polars of all *finite* subsets of X and similarly for the strong topology by taking the polars of all *bounded* subsets, we generalize these ideas in the following exercise.

EXERCISE 2.7   Let X be a locally convex space and consider any collection $\mathcal{G}$ of subsets of X that satisfies:

(a) $G \in \mathcal{G} \implies G$ is bounded.
(b) $G_1, G_2 \in \mathcal{G} \implies G_1 \cup G_2 \in \mathcal{G}$.
(c) $G \in \mathcal{G}$ and $\alpha \neq 0 \implies \alpha G \in \mathcal{G}$.
(d) $\bigcup_{G \in \mathcal{G}} G = X$.

Show that by taking as a neighborhood base at 0 for X^* the collection $\{G^\circ : G \in \mathcal{G}\}$, X^* becomes a locally convex space. Also show that the topology on X^* is intermediate in strength to the weak* and strong topologies, and convergence in the topology is that of uniform convergence (of linear functionals) on members of $\mathcal{G}$. Hint: Use Theorem 2.1.

We list some of the more common topologies that are placed on X^* in this fashion.

Members of $\mathcal{G}$	Name of Topology on X^*
finite subsets of X	weak* topology
bounded subsets of X	strong topology
compact subsets of X	compact–open or uniform convergence on compact sets topology
convex, balanced weakly compact subsets of X	Mackey topology
subsets of X which can be viewed as sequences converging to 0	bounded weak* topology

□ THE BANACH–ALAOGLU THEOREM

We now prove an important theorem about the polar of a neighborhood of 0 in a locally convex space.

THEOREM 2.8 **Banach–Alaoglu Theorem**
Let X be a locally convex space and U a neighborhood 0 in X. Then U° is compact in the weak* topology on X^*.

□ **PROOF**   We may assume without loss of generality that U is a closed, balanced convex neighborhood of 0 since $U^{\circ\circ}$ is, and $U^\circ = (U^{\circ\circ})^\circ$. In this case let ρ be the continuous seminorm obtained as the gauge of U, so that $U = \{x \in X : \rho(x) \leq 1\}$. Then

$$U^\circ = \{f \in X^* : |f(x)| \leq 1 \text{ for all } x \in U\},$$

and by Lemma 1.6d,

$$U^\circ = \{f \in X^* : |f(x)| \leq \rho(x) \text{ for all } x \in X\}.$$

Since $|f(x)| \leq \rho(x)$ implies the continuity of f, we may finally write

$$U^\circ = \{f:X \to \mathbf{K}, f \text{ linear} : |f(x)| \leq \rho(x) \text{ for all } x \in X\}.$$

For each $x \in X$, define

$$D_x = \{\alpha \in \mathbf{K} : |\alpha| \leq \rho(x)\}$$

and define $T = \Pi_{x \in X} D_x$. Then T is a compact topological space as the Cartesian product of the compact disks D_x in $\mathbf{K}$ (Tychonoff's theorem). Recall that a subbase for the topology of T consists of subsets of the form $V = \Pi_{x \in X} V_x$, where each V_x is open in D_x and all but *one* of them is D_x. We shall view T in a slightly different but equivalent manner as follows: Each point in T can be regarded as a function $F : X \to \mathbf{K}$ such that $F(x) \in D_x$ for all $x \in X$. Hence

$$T = \{F:X \to \mathbf{K} : |F(x)| \leq \rho(x) \qquad \text{for all } x \in X\}.$$

The product topology on T then becomes the weakest topology such that for each $x \in X$ the "coordinate" projection $\hat{x}: T \to D_x$ defined by $\hat{x}(F) = F(x)$ is continuous. In this light,

$$U^\circ = \{f:X \to \mathbf{K}, f \text{ linear} : |f(x)| \leq \rho(x) \qquad \text{for all } x \in X\}$$

is a subset of the compact space T (those $F \in T$ that are linear) and the relative weak* topology on U° is precisely the relative topology on U° as a subset of T. Hence it will follow that U° must be weak* compact if we can show that U° is closed in the relative topology on T. (A closed subset of a compact set is compact.) However,

$$U^\circ = \bigcap_{\substack{\alpha,\beta \in \mathbf{K} \\ x,y \in X}} \ker((\widehat{\alpha x + \beta y}) - \alpha \hat{x} - \beta \hat{y}),$$

which is an intersection of closed sets in T (kernels of continuous functions on T), and hence is closed in T. This completes the proof.

Applications of this theorem will be presented in Chapters 3 and 6. Another application forms part of the Mackey–Arens theorem, which will be remarked upon at the end of this chapter.

□ DISTRIBUTION THEORY

We first introduce some definitions and results that will enable us to define the idea of a distribution or generalized function.

Let $\{X_i\}_{i=1}^{\infty}$ be a family of locally convex spaces with the property that $i < j \Rightarrow X_i \subseteq X_j$ and the topology of X_i coincides with its relative topology as a subspace of X_j. Let $X = \bigcup_{i=1}^{\infty} X_i$, and topologize X as follows: A neighborhood base at 0 consists of all balanced convex subsets U of X for which $U \cap X_i$ is a neighborhood of 0 in X_i for every $i = 1, 2, \ldots$. A space X topologized in this fashion is called the *inductive limit* of the locally convex spaces $\{X_i\}$.

THEOREM 2.9 The inductive limit space X as defined above is a locally convex tls. A linear functional or a seminorm on X is continuous if and only if its restriction to each X_i is continuous.

□ **PROOF** Let $\mathfrak{F}$ be the collection of all balanced convex subsets U of X for which $U \cap X_i$ is a neighborhood of 0 in X_i, $i = 1, 2, \ldots$. It is readily checked that $\mathfrak{F}$ is a nonempty collection that satisfies (a)–(d) of Theorem 2.1. Note that each $U \in \mathfrak{F}$ is absorbing by the condition on the $U \cap X_i$. The conversely part of this theorem can thus be applied to conclude that X with the inductive limit topology is a locally convex tls. (We do not prove that X is also Hausdorff and hence a locally convex space, though this is the case.) If f is a continuous linear functional on X, then f is bounded on a neighborhood U of 0 (Lemma 2.4a), and hence $f|_{X_i}$ is bounded on $U \cap X_i$ for all $i = 1, 2, \ldots$. Since $U \cap X_i$ is, by nature of the inductive topology on X, a neighborhood of 0 in X_i, $f|_{X_i}$ is continuous on X_i. Conversely, if f is a linear functional on X, and $f|_{X_i}$ is continuous for $i = 1, 2, \ldots$, then for each i there exists a balanced convex neighborhood U_i of 0 in X_i such that $f|X_i$ is bounded by 1 on U_i. Letting $V = \bigcup_{i=1}^{\infty} U_i$ and $U = \mathrm{CH}(V)$, then U is a neighborhood of 0 in X (why?), f is bounded by 1 on U and hence f is continuous on X. (Note that if f is bounded by 1 on V it must be bounded by 1 on $\mathrm{CH}(V)$.) The proof for seminorms is identical.

We now apply these ideas to a concrete situation as follows. Let $\mathfrak{C}_o^\infty(\mathbf{R}^n)$ denote the collection of all infinitely differentiable real- or complex-valued functions on $\mathbf{R}^n$ each of which vanishes on the complement of some compact set (the compact set may depend on the function). Choose any increasing sequence $\{K_i\}_{i=1}^\infty$ of compact subsets of $\mathbf{R}^n$ whose union is $\mathbf{R}^n$, and consider the locally convex spaces $\mathfrak{D}_{K_i}(\mathbf{R}^n)$ as described in the early part of this chapter. Then $\bigcup_{i=1}^\infty \mathfrak{D}_{K_i}(\mathbf{R}^n) = \mathfrak{C}_o^\infty(\mathbf{R}^n)$, and the conditions are satisfied for applying the inductive limit construction.

Let $\mathfrak{D}(\mathbf{R}^n)$ denote the locally convex tls that is obtained by topologizing $\mathfrak{C}_o^\infty(\mathbf{R}^n)$ in this manner. A pleasant fact is that the seminorm ρ on $\mathfrak{D}(\mathbf{R}^n)$ defined by $\rho(f) = \sup_{x \in \mathbf{R}^n} |f(x)|$ is continuous. Indeed, restricting ρ to each space $\mathfrak{D}_{K_i}(\mathbf{R}^n)$, we obtain $\rho_{K_i,0}$; recall that

$$\rho_{K_i,m}(f) = \sup_{\substack{|s| \le m \\ x \in K_i}} |D^s f(x)|.$$

Since $\rho_{K_i,0}$ is continuous by definition of the topology on $\mathfrak{D}_{K_i}(\mathbf{R}^n)$, Theorem 2.9 shows that ρ is continuous.

An even more plesant consequence of the above fact is that $\rho(f) = 0 \Longrightarrow f = 0$ so that $\mathfrak{D}(\mathbf{R}^n)$ is a locally convex space ($\{\rho\}$ is a total one-member subcollection of the collection of continuous seminorms on $\mathfrak{D}(\mathbf{R}^n)$).

Members of $\mathfrak{D}(\mathbf{R}^n)$ are traditionally called *test functions* and a continuous linear functional T on the locally convex space $\mathfrak{D}(\mathbf{R}^n)$ is called a *generalized function* or *distribution* in $\mathbf{R}^n$. Thus $(\mathfrak{D}(\mathbf{R}^n))^*$ is called a distribution space.

Distributions are playing an increasingly important role in various areas of pure and applied mathematics, and what follows will be a brief attempt (most proofs omitted) at showing how some of these ideas are used.

We begin with two examples of distributions.

1. Let φ be any real- or complex-valued function on $\mathbf{R}^n$ such that $\int_K |\varphi| < \infty$ for every compact subset K of $\mathbf{R}^n$. Define T_φ on $\mathfrak{D}(\mathbf{R}^n)$ by

$$T_\varphi(f) = \int_{\mathbf{R}^n} \varphi f.$$

Then $T_\varphi \in (\mathfrak{D}(\mathbf{R}^n))^*$, and hence is a distribution in $\mathbf{R}^n$. Such distributions are called *distribution functions*. The *Heaviside distribution* in $\mathbf{R}$ is T_H where

$$H(x) = \begin{cases} 1 & \text{if } x \geq 0 \\ 0 & \text{if } x < 0 \end{cases}$$

is the Heaviside function.

2. Given any $x \in \mathbf{R}^n$, define T_{δ_x} on $\mathfrak{D}(\mathbf{R}^n)$ by

$$T_{\delta_x}(f) = f(x).$$

Then T_{δ_x} is a distribution called the *Dirac distribution* concentrated at x. If $x = 0$, we write T_δ for T_{δ_0}. It can be shown that the Dirac distribution is not a distribution function (the so-called Dirac δ "function" notwithstanding).

Given any distribution T in $\mathbf{R}^n$ (function or otherwise), its *distributional derivative* with respect to x_i is defined by

$$\frac{\partial T}{\partial x_i}(f) = -T\left(\frac{\partial f}{\partial x_i}\right).$$

For any $T \in (\mathfrak{D}(\mathbf{R}^n))^*$, $\partial T / \partial x_i$ can also be shown to be a distribution, and these generalized derivatives obey all the familiar differentiation rules. As an example consider the Heaviside and Dirac distributions in $\mathbf{R}$:

$$\frac{dT_H}{dx}(f) = -T_H\left(\frac{df}{dx}\right) = -\int_0^\infty \frac{df}{dx} =$$

$$f(0) - \lim_{N \to \infty} f(N) = T_\delta(f).$$

Hence the derivative of the Heaviside distribution function in $\mathbf{R}$ is the Dirac distribution in $\mathbf{R}$ (which is not itself a distribution function).

If T_φ is a distribution arising from a differentiable function φ on $\mathbf{R}^n$, then

$$\frac{\partial T_\varphi}{\partial x_i} = T_{\delta\varphi/\delta x_i}$$

The crux of the proof of this important fact is the integration by parts formula, as can be seen from the following verification for distributions in $\mathbf{R}$:

$$\frac{dT_\varphi}{dx}(f) = -T_\varphi\left(\frac{df}{dx}\right) = -\int_{\mathbf{R}} \varphi\frac{df}{dx}$$

$$= \int_{\mathbf{R}} \frac{d\varphi}{dx}\cdot f - \lim_{N\to\infty} \varphi(x)\cdot f(x)\,\Big|_{-N}^{N}$$

$$= \int_{\mathbf{R}} \frac{d\varphi}{dx}\cdot f = T_{d\varphi/dx}(f),$$

where the limit term vanishes since f vanishes outside some compact set.

The thrust of the above result is that the mapping $f \mapsto T_f$ (from differentiable functions on $\mathbf{R}^n$ to $(\mathfrak{D}(\mathbf{R}^n))^*$) preserves differentiation. It is also true that distribution functions are equal if and only if the functions from which they arise are equal except on a set of Lebesgue measure zero. Combining these observations with Exercise 2.8a below, we see that a natural, compelling, and important generalization of the notion of differentiability arises by identifying φ with T_φ (cf. Exercise 2.8b). This generalization process has far-reaching ramifications in analysis, (partial) differential equations, and its cousin, mathematical physics. A few additional remarks on distributions appear at the end of the chapter.

EXERCISE 2.8   a. Show that if T_φ and T_ψ are distribution functions and $\alpha,\beta \in \mathbf{K}$, then $T_{\alpha\varphi+\beta\psi} = \alpha T_\varphi + \beta T_\psi$.

b. Let I be the constant function of value 1 and A the absolute value function on $\mathbf{R}$. Describe dT_A/dx in terms of T_I and T_H.

c. State and prove as much as you can about the relationship between two distribution functions in $\mathbf{R}$ which have the same derivative.

☐ METRIZABILITY AND NORMABILITY

Recall that a topological space is called *metrizable* if there exists on the space a metric that induces its topology. If X is a locally convex space with a countable neighborhood base at 0, let us choose a countable neighborhood base at 0 containing only balanced convex sets. We may thus obtain in the usual manner a countable collection $\{\rho_i\}_{i=1}^{\infty}$ of seminorms that determine the topology on X.

THEOREM 2.10 A locally convex space X with a countable neighborhood base at 0 is metrizable.

□ **PROOF** If $\{\rho_i\}_{i=1}$ is a sequence of seminorms that determine the topology on X, define $\rho = \sum_{i=1}^{\infty} 2^{-i}\rho_i/(1 + \rho_i)$. Then (check this if you have not seen it before) each term $\rho_i/(1 + \rho_i)$ satisfies the triangle inequality, and $d(x,y) = \rho(x - y)$ is on X a metric that is clearly translation invariant. We wish to show that the topology on X induced by d is its original locally convex space topology. Indeed if

$$U = \{x \in X : \rho_{k_i}(x) < \epsilon, \quad i = 1, \ldots, n, \quad 0 < \epsilon < 1\}$$

is a basic neighborhood of 0 in X (original topology), then choosing $m = 1 + \max\{k_1, \ldots, k_n\}$, we obtain $\{x \in X : d(x,0) < \epsilon/2^m\} \subseteq U$ by the following calculation: $d(x,0) < \epsilon/2^m \Rightarrow \rho_{k_i}(x) < 1$ and hence

$$\tfrac{1}{2}\rho_{k_i}(x) < \frac{\rho_{k_i}(x)}{1 + \rho_{k_i}(x)} < \frac{2^{k_i}\epsilon}{2^m} \Rightarrow \rho_{k_i}(x) < \epsilon \Rightarrow x \in U.$$

Thus the metric topology is at least as strong as the original. Conversely, if $V = \{x \in X : d(x,0) < \epsilon\}$, choose n such that $2^{-n} < \epsilon/2$, and then

$$\{x \in X : \rho_i(x) < \epsilon/2, \ 1 = 1,2, \ldots, n\} \subseteq V.$$

Hence the topologies induced by $\{\rho_i\}_{i=1}^{\infty}$ and d are identical at 0, and hence everywhere by translation invariance.

Note that $\rho(x) = d(x,0)$ is not a seminorm on X, so a first countable (i.e., countable neighborhood base at 0) locally convex space need not be normable. However:

EXERCISE 2.9   If a finite number of seminorms $\{\rho_i\}_{i=1}^n$ generate the topology of a locally convex space X, then X "is" a normed linear space, i.e., one can find on X a single norm that induces its topology.

An even better characterization of those locally convex spaces that are normable is

THEOREM 2.11   If a locally convex space X has a bounded neighborhood of 0, then X is a normed linear space.

□ **PROOF**   If V is the bounded neighborhood of 0, choose a balanced convex neighborhood U of 0 with $U \subseteq V$. Let ρ be the gauge of U. We will show that the topology induced by ρ alone is the original locally convex space topology on X. It is clear that every neighborhood of 0 induced by ρ is a neighborhood in the original topology since ρ is continuous. Conversely, if W is a neighborhood of 0 in the original topology, there exists $\alpha > 0$ such that $U \subseteq \alpha W$ by the boundedness of U. Thus $(1/\alpha)U \subseteq W$ and $\{x \in X : \rho(x) < 1/\alpha\} \subseteq W$, so ρ does indeed define the original locally convex space topology on X, and X is normable.

Note that conversely, every normed linear space has an obvious supply of bounded neighborhoods of 0. We thus conclude (with the aid of Problem 2, Chapter 1) that $\mathfrak{A}(D)$ is not a normable locally convex space.

We now proceed in our course of increasingly specialized spaces to the study of normed linear spaces and Banach spaces.

□ **REMARKS**

Concerning the polar of a subset A of a locally convex space X, more is true than was proved in Theorem 2.7b. It can be shown using a separation theorem of the type mentioned in the Remarks in Chapter 1 that $A^{\circ\circ}$ is the *smallest* closed, balanced convex set containing A [4, p. 238].

We have shown that $(X_w^*)^* = X$, but (Problem 2, Chapter 3) this may not be the case for $(X_s^*)^*$. If τ is a locally convex space topology on X^* for which $(X^*, \tau)^* = X$, then the Banach–Alaoglu theorem (which was stated as a result about the polars of neighborhoods of 0 in X) can be carried over to a statement about neighborhoods of 0 in X^*. Specifically it says that if N is a τ neighborhood of 0 in X^*, then N° is weakly compact in X (this requires some duality-type thought). Assuming with no loss of generality that N was a closed, balanced convex τ neighborhood of 0 in X^* and using the assertion of the first paragraph of these remarks, we conclude that $N = (N^\circ)^\circ$ and hence that our τ neighborhood N is itself the polar of the balanced, convex, *weakly compact* subset N° of X. Recalling the definition of the Mackey topology on X^*, we conclude that the τ topology we started with is intermediate in strength to the weak* and Mackey topologies.

The elegant completion of this circle of ideas lies in the *Mackey–Arens theorem:* A locally convex space topology τ on X^* is such that $(X^*, \tau)^* = X$ if and only if τ is between the weak* and the Mackey topologies on X^*. (Above we argued the "only if" part.) For a development of this theorem see Wilansky's *Functional Analysis* [4, pp. 246–248].

The theory of distributions was first developed by L. Schwartz (*circa* 1950–1951). It has revolutionized treatments of (partial) differential equations by inviting the investigation of "weak" or distribution solutions to such equations instead of standard function sulutions. Thus if there is on **R** a function φ that is not the derivative of any other function, the differential equation $dT/dx = T_\varphi$ may have a distribution solution. Likewise if $h : \mathbf{R}^2 \rightarrow \mathbf{R}$ is a function of x only, it clearly satisfies the partial differential equation $\partial^2 h / \partial x\, \partial y = 0$ (differentiate first with respect to y), but it may not (if its partial with respect to x fails to exist) satisfy $\partial^2 h / \partial y\, \partial x = 0$. This dependence on the order of things is awkward, and can be avoided with the use of distributions.

A clear exposition of some of the ideas behind distribution theory appears in articles by Horvath [5] and Treves [6]. Some of the details that we omitted can be found in Yosida's book [7, pp. 28–30 and pp. 46–52]. Also Horvath's book [8] provides a topological linear space approach to distributions.

We proved in Exercise 1.5b that if X and Y are topological linear spaces and the linear transformation $T : X \rightarrow Y$ is continuous, then T maps bounded sets onto bounded sets. Problems 4, 5, and 6 introduce the idea of a *bornologic* locally convex space and examine the converse of the above result for T.

☐ **PROBLEMS**

1. Let $\mathcal{C}(\mathbf{R})$ denote the continuous real-valued functions on $\mathbf{R}$ topologized by the seminorms $\{\rho_K\}$ with K a compact subset of $\mathbf{R}$ ($\rho_K(f) = \sup_{x \in K} |f(x)|$). Let $T: \mathcal{C}(\mathbf{R}) \to \mathcal{C}(\mathbf{R})$ be the mapping that multiplies by the identity function on $\mathbf{R}: (Tf)x = xf(x)$. Prove that T is a continuous linear transformation. Hint: Use Theorem 2.3 and the fact that any constant multiple of a continuous seminorm is also a continuous seminorm.

2. Let $X = \{f:[0,1] \to \mathbf{R} : f$ bounded and Riemann integrable$\}$. Topologize X by the proposed metric $d(f,g) = \int_0^1 |f - g|^{1/2}$.

   a. Prove that d is in fact a translation invariant metric on X.
   b. Prove that X is a Hausdorff tls.
   c. Show that X has no proper convex neighborhoods of 0.

   Hint: Consider any basic neighborhood $U = \{f \in X : d(f,0) < r\}$ of 0. Let g be any member of X and show that $g \in$ CH(U) by partitioning $[0,1]$ into n equal intervals, letting

$$g_i = \begin{cases} g & \text{on the } i\text{th interval} \\ 0 & \text{elsewhere,} \end{cases}$$

   and considering

$$g = \frac{1}{n}\left(\frac{g_1}{n}\right) + \frac{1}{n}\left(\frac{g_2}{n}\right) + \cdots + \frac{1}{n}\left(\frac{g_n}{n}\right).$$

   A clever choice of n will use the fact that f is bounded on $[0,1]$.

   d. Conclude that X has no nonzero continuous linear functionals and cannot be a locally convex space.

3. Show that there exist infinite dimensional locally convex spaces all of whose linear functionals are continuous. Hint: If X is any infinite-dimensional linear space, there is on X an obvious locally convex space topology that will do the job.

4. We say a subset U of a tls X *absorbs* a subset B of X if there exists $\alpha > 0$ such that $B \subseteq \alpha U$. Recall then that a bounded set is one that is absorbed by every neighborhood of 0. A sub-

set U of X will be called *bornivorous* if it absorbs all bounded subsets of X. A locally convex space X is *bornologic* if every bornivorous, balanced convex subset of X is a neighborhood of 0.

    a. Show that any normed linear space is bornologic.

    b. Show that $\mathfrak{D}(\mathbf{R}^n)$ is bornologic.

5. Prove that a locally convex space X is bornologic if and only if every seminorm (and hence every linear functional) that is bounded on all bounded sets is continuous.

6. Let X be a bornologic locally convex space and Y a locally convex space, and let $T : X \rightarrow Y$ be a linear transformation. Prove that T maps bounded sets to bounded sets if and only if T is continuous.

Banach Spaces

3

□ QUOTIENT SPACES

A Banach space X, we recall, is a normed linear space that is complete with respect to its norm-induced metric. Thus X has defined on it a function $\| \ \| : X \to \mathbf{R}$ satisfying for all $\alpha \in \mathbf{K}$ and $x, y \in X$

(a) $\| \alpha x \| = | \alpha | \ \| x \|$
(b) $\| x + y \| \leq \| x \| + \| y \|$
(c) $\| x \| \geq 0$ and $\| x \| = 0 \Rightarrow x = 0$;

and completeness in X means that every $\| \ \|$ Cauchy sequence is $\| \ \|$ convergent. In what follows we do not make the assumption that X is complete except when specified.

The basic open neighborhoods of 0 in X can simply be chosen as the open balls

$$B_{1/n} = \{x \in X : \| x \| < 1/n\} \qquad (n = 1, 2, \ldots),$$

so X is a first countable space. By what was done in Chapter 2, X is certainly a locally convex space, and the norm is continuous. In the presence of first countability this continuity is equivalent to sequential continuity, i.e., $x_n \to x \Rightarrow \| x_n \| \to \| x \|$. (Note that $x_n \to x$ in X means, by definition, $\| x - x_n \| \to 0$.)

EXERCISE 3.1 Prove directly from the axioms for a norm that

a. Addition is continuous:

$$x_n \to x \qquad \text{and} \qquad y_n \to y \Rightarrow x_n + y_n \to x + y.$$

b. Scalar multiplication is continuous:

$$\alpha_n \to \alpha \qquad \text{and} \qquad x_n \to x \Rightarrow \alpha_n x_n \to \alpha x.$$

c. The norm is continuous: $x_n \to x \Rightarrow \| x_n \| \to \| x \|$.

Returning briefly to a more general situation, let X be any linear space and let M be a subspace of X. Then we can form the *quotient space* X/M consisting of equivalence classes of members of X formed by the equivalence relation

$$x_1 \sim x_2 \Leftrightarrow x_1 - x_2 \in M.$$

We denote the equivalence class containing x by $x + M$. We do not prove the standard result that X/M is a linear space under the well-defined operations $\oplus$ and $\odot$ defined by $(x_1 + M) \oplus (x_2 + M) = (x_1 + x_2) + M$ and $\alpha \odot (x + M) = (\alpha x) + M$. The quotient map $Q : X \to X/M$ defined by $Q(x) = x + M$ is then readily seen to be a linear transformation.

As indicated in the Remarks in Chapter 1, it is possible to prove various expected results about X/M in various topological settings, but we content ourselves with one of these. Note that a *seminormed linear space* is simply a tls whose topology is generated by a single seminorm.

THEOREM 3.1 Let X be a seminormed linear space with generating seminorm ρ and let M be a closed subspace on X. Then the function $\| \ \| : X/M \to \mathbf{R}$ defined by $\|x + M\| = \inf_{m \in M} \{\rho(x + m)\}$ makes X/M into a normed linear space. If X is complete (with respect to ρ), then X/M is complete and hence a Banach space.

□ **PROOF** We first show that $\| \ \|$ is indeed a norm. Thus

$$\| \alpha \odot (x + M) \| = \| \alpha x + M \| = \inf_{m \in M} \{\rho(\alpha x + m)\}$$

$$= \inf_{m \in M} \{\rho(\alpha x + \alpha m)\}$$

$$= |\alpha| \inf_{m \in M} \{\rho(x + m)\}$$

$$= |\alpha| \ \|x + M\|.$$

The triangle inequality results from

$$\| (x + M) \oplus (y + M) \| = \| x + y + M \|$$

$$= \inf_{m \in M} \{\rho(x + y + m)\}$$

$$= \inf_{m_1, m_2 \in M} \{\rho(x + m_1 + y + m_2)\}$$

$$\leq \inf_{m_1, m_2 \in M} \{\rho(x + m_1) + \rho(y + m_2)\}$$

$$= \inf_{m_1 \in M} \{\rho(x + m_1)\}$$

$$+ \inf_{m_2 \in M} \{\rho(y + m_2)\}$$

$$= \| x + M \| + \| y + M \|.$$

Finally, it is clear that $\| x + M \| \geq 0$ for all $x \in X/M$, and $\| x + M \| = 0 \Rightarrow$ there exists a sequence $\{m_i\}_{i=1}^{\infty}$ in M such that $\rho(x + m_i) \rightarrow 0 \Rightarrow -m_i \rightarrow x \Rightarrow$ (since M is closed) $x \in M \Rightarrow x + M = 0$. To show that X/M is complete when X is, we start with a Cauchy sequence in X/M, call it $\{x_i + M\}_{i=1}^{\infty}$. We first choose a subsequence $\{x_{i_k} + M\}_{k=1}^{\infty}$ of this Cauchy sequence such that $\| (x_{i_k} + M) \ominus (x_{i_{k+1}} + M) \| < 2^{-k}$, $k = 1, 2, \ldots$. This can always be done by the definition of "Cauchy." We can now inductively obtain a sequence y_k in X such that $y_k \in x_{i_k} + M$ and $\rho(y_k - y_{k+1}) < 2^{-k}$. Indeed we may choose any $y_1 \in x_{i_1} + M$ to get started, and if y_k has been suitably chosen, a suitable y_{k+1} can always be chosen since

$$\inf_{m \in M} \{ \rho(y_k - (x_{i_{k+1}} + m)) \} = \| (y_k - x_{i_{k+1}}) + M \|$$
$$= \| (y_k + M) \ominus (x_{i_{k+1}} + M) \|$$
$$= \| (x_{i_k} + M) \ominus (x_{i_{k+1}} + M) \|$$
$$< 2^{-k}.$$

It is easily checked that the sequence $\{y_k\}_{k=1}^{\infty}$ so obtained is Cauchy in X; and since X is complete, $y_k \rightarrow y$ for some $y \in X$. Since

$$\| (x_{i_k} + M) \ominus (y + M) \|$$
$$= \| (y_k + M) \ominus (y + M) \| \leq \rho(y_k - y)$$

we have $(x_{i_k} + M) \rightarrow y + M$ where $\{x_{i_k} + M\}_{k=1}^{\infty}$ is a subsequence of our original Cauchy sequence. Finally, we note that if a subsequence of a Cauchy sequence converges, the sequence itself must do so. Thus our original Cauchy sequence converges and X/M is complete.

EXERCISE 3.2 Prove as was claimed in the above theorem that in any metric space a Cauchy sequence with a convergent subsequence must itself be convergent.

☐ **EXAMPLES**

We describe two general types of Banach spaces. The first depends upon the idea of the Lebesgue integral whose theory will be developed in Chapter 4. For now it will do no harm to keep in mind the familiar Riemann integral.

1. Given $p \in \mathbf{R}$, $1 \leq p < \infty$. and a subset S of $\mathbf{R}$, define $\mathcal{L}^p(S)$ to be all Lebesgue integrable $\mathbf{K}$-valued functions f on S such that

$$\rho(f) = (\int_S |f|^p)^{1/p} < \infty,$$

and let $M = \{f \in \mathcal{L}^p(S) : \rho(f) = 0\}$. It will be shown (using Theorem 3.1) in Chapter 4 that $L^p(S) = \mathcal{L}^p(S)/M$ is a Banach space.

Some simpler related examples which require no measure theory (and no quotient space) arise by considering sequences $\alpha = \{\alpha_i\}_{i=1}^{\infty}$, $\alpha_i \in \mathbf{K}$, to obtain the l^p spaces ($1 \leq p < \infty$). Thus

$$l^p = \left\{\alpha : \|\alpha\|_p = \left(\sum_{i=1}^{\infty} |\alpha_i|^p\right)^{1/p} < \infty\right\}.$$

Another related Banach space is the space of bounded sequences,

$$l^{\infty} = \{\alpha : \|\alpha\|_{\infty} = \sup_i \{|\alpha_i|\} < \infty\}.$$

Note by way of illustration that the harmonic sequence $\alpha = \{1/n\}_{n=1}^{\infty}$ has the property that $\alpha \notin l^1$, but $\alpha \in l^p$ for all $\rho > 1$. It can be shown generally that $p_1 < p_2 \implies l^{p_1} \subseteq l^{p_2}$ and that $\| \ \|_{p_1} \geq \| \ \|_{p_2}$ on p^{p_1}. Furthermore, it turns out that for $\alpha \in l^1$, $\|\alpha\|_{\infty} = \lim_{p \to \infty} \|\alpha\|_p$, thus justifying the notation for l^{∞}. Both the L^p and l^p spaces mentioned above and some of their important properties will emerge from the general treatment of integration theory in Chapter 4.

2. Let S be any topological space and let $\mathcal{C}(S)$ be the linear space of all *bounded*, continuous $\mathbf{K}$-valued functions on S. For $f \in \mathcal{C}(S)$ define $\|f\| = \sup_{s \in S} |f(s)|$. Then $\mathcal{C}(S)$ is a Banach space. (This was proved for $S = [0,1]$ in Exercise 1.4c and d, but the proof carries over without alteration to our general setting.) Note that convergence under $\| \ \|$ is, in familiar cases, uniform convergence. Also note that if $\mathcal{N}$ denotes the positive integers with the discrete topology, $\mathcal{C}(\mathcal{N})$ is precisely l^{∞} as defined in the preceding paragraph.

□ THE SPACE $\mathfrak{B}(X,Y)$

THEOREM 3.2 Given X and Y normed linear spaces and $T:X \to Y$ a linear transformation, then the following are equivalent.

    a. T is continuous.
    b. T is continuous at 0.
    c. $\|x_n\| \to 0 \Rightarrow \|Tx_n\| \to 0$.
    d. There exists $K \geq 0$ such that $\|Tx\| \leq K\|x\|$ for all $x \in X$.
    e. T maps bounded sets onto bounded sets.

□   **PROOF**   (a) $\Longleftrightarrow$ (b) and (b) $\Longrightarrow$ (c) are clear.

(c) $\Longrightarrow$ (d): If (d) were false, then for each proposed $K = n$, $n = 1, 2, \ldots$, we could choose $x_n \in X$ such that $\|Tx_n\| > n\|x_n\|$. Setting $y_n = x_n/(n\|x_n\|)$, $\|y_n\| \to 0$, but $\|Ty_n\| > 1$ for all n, contradicting (c).

(d) $\Longrightarrow$ (e): We use the metric definition of bounded set, so B bounded means $\sup_{x \in B}\|x\| < \infty$. But see Exercise 3.4a. If (d) holds, then for a bounded set $B \subseteq X$,

$$\sup_{x \in B}\|Tx\| \leq K \cdot \sup_{x \in B}\|x\| < \infty.$$

Hence $T(B)$ is bounded.

(e) $\Longrightarrow$ (b): Given a neighborhood $C_\epsilon = \{y \in Y : \|y\| < \epsilon\}$ of 0 in Y, let B_1 denote the open unit ball in X ($B_1 = \{x \in X : \|x\| < 1\}$). Since $T(B_1)$ is bounded in Y, there exists $\alpha > 0$ such that $T(B_1) \subseteq \alpha C_\epsilon$ and hence $T(\alpha^{-1}B_1) \subseteq C_\epsilon$. Since $\alpha^{-1}B_1$ is a neighborhood of 0 in X, we have proved that T is continuous at 0. (Note that this result also follows neatly from Problems 4a and 6 at the end of Chapter 2.)

EXERCISE 3.3 Two norms $\|\ \|_1$ and $\|\ \|_2$ on a linear space X are defined to be *equivalent* if they generate the same topology on X. Prove that $\|\ \|_1$ and $\|\ \|_2$ are equivalent if and only if there exist constants $K, K' > 0$ such that $K\|x\|_1 \leq \|x\|_2 \leq K'\|x\|_1$ for all $x \in X$. Hint: Use (a) and (b) of Theorem 3.2 applied to the identity map $T: (X, \|\ \|_1) \to (X, \|\ \|_2)$.

We denote the linear space of all continuous linear transformations between X and Y by $\mathscr{B}(X, Y)$. Members of this space are frequently called *bounded* linear transformations in view of (d) and (e) of Theorem 3.2. Given $T \in \mathscr{B}(X, Y)$, we define $\| T \| = \sup_{\|x\| \le 1} \| Tx \|$ (the multiple use of $\| \ \|$ should cause no confusion). Note that $\| T \|$ is finite by Theorem 3.2d (indeed $\| T \| \le K$) and that it suffices to work with $\| x \| = 1$ rather than $\| x \| \le 1$ in the definition of $\| T \|$.

EXERCISE 3.4   a. Let B be a subset of a normed linear space X. Prove that B is bounded in the norm or metric space sense ($\sup_{x \in B} \| x \| < \infty$) if and only if B is bounded in the tls sense (given a neighborhood U of 0 there exists $\alpha > 0$ such that $B \subset \alpha U$).

b. Choose for both X and Y the space $\mathscr{C}([0, 1])$ of continuous real-valued functions on $[0, 1]$ with the sup norm. Define $T: X \to X$ by $(Tf)(t) = e^t \cdot f(t)$, $t \in [0, 1]$. Prove that $T \in \mathscr{B}(X, X)$ and compute $\| T \|$.

THEOREM 3.3   As defined above, $\| \ \|$ makes $\mathscr{B}(X, Y)$ into a normed linear space, and $T \in \mathscr{B}(X, Y) \Rightarrow \| Tx \| \le \| T \| \ \| x \|$ for all $x \in X$.

□ **PROOF**   The fact that $\| \ \|$ defines a norm on $\mathscr{B}(X, Y)$ follows essentially from the fact that $\| \ \|$ is a norm on Y. We prove only the triangle inequality. Given $S, T \in \mathscr{B}(X, Y)$,

$$\| S + T \| = \sup_{\|x\| \le 1} \| (S + T)x \| = \sup_{\|x\| \le 1} \| Sx + Tx \|$$
$$\le \sup_{\|x\| \le 1} \{ \| Sx \| + \| Tx \| \} \le \sup_{\|x\| \le 1} \| Sx \| + \sup_{\|x\| \le 1} \| Tx \|$$
$$= \| S \| + \| T \|.$$

Finally, the inequality stated in the theorem follows by observing that for any $x \ne 0$, $x / \| x \|$ always has norm 1. Hence $\| Tx \| / \| x \| = T(x / \| x \|) \le \| T \|$, so that $\| Tx \| \le \| T \| \ \| x \|$.

THEOREM 3.4   Let X be a normed linear space and Y a Banach space. Then $\mathscr{B}(X, Y)$ is a Banach space.

□ **PROOF**   Let $\{ T_n \}_{n=1}^{\infty}$ be a Cauchy sequence in $\mathscr{B}(X, Y)$ and let x be any member of X. Then $\| T_m x - T_n x \| = \| (T_m - T_n)x \| \le$

$\| T_m - T_n \| \, \| x \|$, so $\{ T_n x \}$ is a Cauchy sequence in Y. Since Y is complete, $T_n x \to y$ for some $y \in Y$, and we thus define $T: X \to Y$ by $Tx = y$. T is linear since

$$
\begin{aligned}
T(\alpha_1 x_1 + \alpha_2 x_2) &= \lim \{ T_n (\alpha_1 x_1 + \alpha_2 x_2) \} \\
&= \lim \{ \alpha_1 T_n x_1 + \alpha_2 T_n x_2 \} = \alpha_1 Tx_1 + \alpha_2 Tx_2.
\end{aligned}
$$

To see that $T \in \mathcal{B}(X, Y)$ note that for all $x \in X$,

$$
\| Tx \| = \| \lim_n T_n x \| \leq \sup_n \{ \| T_n \| \, \| x \| \} = (\sup_n \| T_n \|) \| x \|.
$$

Since $\{ T_n \}$ is a Cauchy sequence, the sup is finite, so that T is continuous by Theorem 3.2d. Finally, we must show that $T_n \xrightarrow{\| \ \|} T$ or that $\| T - T_n \| \to 0$. Given $\epsilon > 0$ choose N such that $m, n > N \Rightarrow \| T_m - T_n \| < \epsilon$. Then

$$
\begin{aligned}
\| (T - T_n) x \| &= \| \lim_m (T_m - T_n) x \| \\
&= \lim_m \| (T_m - T_n) x \| \leq \epsilon \| x \|,
\end{aligned}
$$

so $\| T - T_n \| \to 0$.

□ CONJUGATE SPACES AND REFLEXIVITY

If we choose $Y = \mathbf{K}$, then $\mathcal{B}(X, Y)$ becomes X^*, the conjugate space of X. By Theorem 3.4, X^* with its normed topology is always a Banach space since $\mathbf{K}$ is complete.

For emphasis, we now restate the Hahn–Banach theorem in the most pleasant setting of a normed linear space X.

THEOREM 3.5   Hahn–Banach Theorem
Let M be a subspace of X and $g \in M^*$. Then g can be extended to $f \in X^*$ such that $\| f \| = \| g \|_M$ ($\| \ \|_M$ is the norm restricted to M).

□ **PROOF**   There is no loss of generality in assuming that $\| g \|_M = 1$ so that $| g(x) | \leq \| x \|$ for all $x \in M$. Then the Hahn–Banach theorem (Theorem 1.8) applied to g and the norm $\| \ \|$ on X yields the desired f.

COROLLARY   For any nonzero $x_0 \in X$, there exists $f \in X^*$ such that $\|f\| = 1$ and $f(x_0) = \|x_0\|$.

□   **PROOF**   Let $M = \text{span } \{x_0\}$ and define g on M by $g(\alpha x_0) = \alpha g(x_0) = \alpha \|x_0\|$. Then $\|g\|_M = 1$, and an application of the Hahn–Banach theorem yields the desired $f \in X^*$.

Unless otherwise stated, we shall always assume that the conjugate space X^* of a normed linear space X is endowed with its norm topology. Since the closed unit ball in X^* is simply the polar of the closed unit ball in X (indeed,

$$U = \{x \in X : \|x\| \leq 1\}$$
$$\Longrightarrow U^\circ = \{f \in X^* : |f(x)| \leq 1 \text{ for all } \|x\| \leq 1\}$$
$$\Longrightarrow U^\circ = \{f \in X^* : \|f\| \leq 1\}),$$

it is not difficult to see that this norm topology is precisely the strong topology on X^* as defined in our more general discussion of topologies on the conjugate space of a locally convex space. In that discussion we showed (Exercise 2.6) that the mapping $\blacktriangle : X \to (X^*_s)^*$ is a linear injection (recall $\hat{x}(f) = f(x)$, $f \in X^*$). For normed linear spaces, we can say more:

THEOREM 3.6   Given a normed linear space X, the linear injection $x \longmapsto \hat{x}$ of X into X^{**} is an *isometry*, i.e., $\|\hat{x}\| = \|x\|$ for all $x \in X$.

□   **PROOF**   Let x be any member of X. Then

$$\|\hat{x}\| = \sup_{\substack{f \in X^* \\ \|f\| \leq 1}} |\hat{x}(f)|$$

$$= \sup_{\substack{f \in X^* \\ \|f\| \leq 1}} |f(x)| \leq \sup_{\substack{f \in X^* \\ \|f\| \leq 1}} \|f\| \, \|x\| = \|x\|,$$

where the inequality results from Theorem 3.3. Conversely, the above corollary to the Hahn–Banach theorem ensures the existence of an $f \in X^*$ such that $\|f\| = 1$ and $|f(x)| = \|x\|$. Using this particular f, the final inequality in the above chain becomes an equality, so $\|\hat{x}\| = \|x\|$.

A locally convex space was defined to be *reflexive* if the mapping

⋏: $X \to X^{**}$ (strong topologies) is a homeomorphism. In our normed case reflexivity means that X and X^{**} are not only homeomorphic under ⋏, but (says Theorem 3.6) *isometrically isomorphic,* the natural extension of linear space isomorphism to normed linear spaces. Thus to show reflexivity in the normed setting it suffices to show that ⋏ is surjective, for then the norm-preserving nature of ⋏ will guarantee the continuity of ⋏ and of ⋏⁻¹. As an important class of examples of reflexive spaces we note (proofs to be supplied in Chapter 4) that for $1 < p < \infty$, the spaces $L^p(S)$ mentioned earlier are reflexive as a consequence of the fact that $(L^p(S))^* = L^q(S)$, where $1/p + 1/q = 1$.

EXERCISE 3.5 Let X be a Banach space. Prove X is reflexive $\Longleftrightarrow X^*$ is reflexive. Comment on why this might not be true if X is merely a normed linear space. Hint for $\Longleftarrow$: Assume that X is not reflexive and argue that hence X is a proper closed subspace of X^{**}. Then find in X^{***} an element that is not an $\hat{f}$ for any $f \in X^*$.

To deal more specifically with some of these ideas, we now demonstrate that $(l^1)^* \cong l^\infty$ where $\cong$ indicates a natural isometric isomorphism between these spaces, i.e., every member of l^∞ can be regarded in a natural, linear, and norm-preserving way as a member of $(l^1)^*$ and every member of $(l^1)^*$ is obtainable from a member of l^∞ in this way.

First, if $t = \{t_i\}_{i=1}^\infty \in l^\infty$, then it naturally generates a linear functional t' operating on $\alpha = \{\alpha_i\}_{i=1}^\infty \in l^1$ by the rule $t'(\alpha) = \sum_{i=1}^\infty t_i \alpha_i$. Note that t' is continuous on l^1 (so $t \in (l^1)^*$) since

$$\|t'\| = \sup_{\|\alpha\|_1 = 1} |t'(\alpha)| \leq \sup_i |t_i| = \|t\|_\infty.$$

(The middle inequality is obtained by noting that sup $|t'(\alpha)|$ can be approached by having the sequence α concentrate all its weight on the component corresponding to the "largest" t_i.) Also, the correspondence that associates t' with t is clearly linear. Conversely, if $t'' \in (l^1)^*$, we may define $t = \{t_i\}_{i=1}^\infty$ by $t_i = t(e_i)$ where $e_i \in l^1$ is the sequence which has value 1 in the ith place and 0 elsewhere. It must be shown that if we start with t'', obtain t as indicated, and look at t' as defined above, then $t' = t''$. To see this note that t'' and t' agree on the e_i. Since the tails of sequences in l^1 converge to 0 in l^1 (not true in l^∞), a continuity argument on l^1 shows that t' and t'' agree on all of l^1. Now $\|t\|_\infty = \sup_i |t_i| = \sup_i |t'(e_i)| \le \|t'\|$ (note $\|e_i\|_1 = 1$). Hence $t \in l^\infty$, and by combining the above results the correspondence between $(l^1)^*$ and l^∞ can be seen to be an isometric isomorphism ($\|t'\| = \|t\|_\infty$).

Since the polar of the closed unit ball in a normed linear space X is the closed unit ball in X^*, the Banach–Alaoglu theorem simply states that the (norm) closed unit ball in X^* is compact in the weak* topology. We present two interesting applications of this fact.

THEOREM 3.7 Let X be a normed linear space. Then if X is reflexive, the closed unit ball in X is weakly compact.

□ **PROOF** Let $\bar{B}_1 = \{x \in X : \|x\| \le 1\}$. Since X is reflexive, $\hat{\bar{B}}_1 = \{\hat{x} \in X^{**} : x \in \bar{B}_1\}$ is precisely the closed unit ball in X^{**}. By the Banach Alaoglu theorem applied to X^* and the closed unit ball in X^{**}, $\hat{\bar{B}}_1$ is compact in the weak* topology on X^{**}. But since X is reflexive, this says $\bar{B}_1$ is compact in the weak topology on X. (Note that the weak* topology on X^{**} and the weak topology on X are "identical," both being generated by the members of X^*.)

It turns out that the implication in the above theorem can be strengthened to an equivalence [9, p. 425], thus yielding a useful characterization of reflexivity.

We now present a second and perhaps somewhat surprising application of the Banach–Alaoglu theorem. Its utility is tempered by the fact that not much is known about the subspaces of $\mathcal{C}(S)$, S a compact Hausdorff space.

THEOREM 3.8 Every normed linear space X is isometrically isomorphic to a subspace of $\mathcal{C}(S)$, where S is some compact Hausdorff space. If X is a Banach space, then X is isometrically isomorphic to a closed subspace of $\mathcal{C}(S)$.

□ **PROOF** Let S be the closed unit ball of X^* endowed with the relative weak* topology. Then S is Hausdorff since the weak* topology on X^* is, and S is compact by Banach–Alaoglu. By Theorem 3.6,

$$\|x\| = \|\hat{x}\| = \sup_{\|f\| \leq 1} |\hat{x}(f)| = \sup_{f \in S} |\hat{x}(f)|.$$

Recalling that every x is continuous on X^* and hence on S, we may thus identify $\hat{X}$ with a subspace of $\mathfrak{C}(S)$ endowed with the uniform or sup norm. The first part of the theorem is then established since the identification is clearly linear and injective. If X is complete, then $\hat{X}$ is complete and hence closed as a subspace of $\mathfrak{C}(S)$. This completes the proof.

EXERCISE 3.6   Let X be an infinite-dimensional normed linear space. Prove that the unit circumference $\{f \in X^* : \|f\| = 1\}$ in X^* is weak* dense in the unit ball $\{f \in X^* : \|f\| \leq 1\}$. Hints: Consider any $f \in X^*$ with $\|f\| < 1$ and any weak* basic neighborhood $\mathcal{N} = \{g \in X^* : |\hat{x}_i(f - g)| < \epsilon, \, i = 1, 2, \ldots, n\}$ of f. Use the Hahn–Banach theorem (3.5) to find a $g \in \mathcal{N}$ such that $\|g\| = 1$.

□ OPEN MAPPING, CLOSED GRAPH, AND UNIFORM BOUNDEDNESS THEOREMS

We now proceed to justify our frequent but so far seldom needed reference to Banach spaces by proving three important theorems for which completeness is a vital hypothesis. We first state the topological result known as Baire's category theorem, which will be used in proving several of the results to follow.

THEOREM 3.9   Baire Category Theorem
A complete metric space cannot be represented as the countable union of closed subsets all having empty interior.

EXERCISE 3.7   a. If X is a tls, then the only subspace of X having nonempty interior is X itself.
b. The vector space (or *Hamel*) dimension of a Banach space is either finite or uncountable. Hint: Use the fact (Problem 5, Chapter 1) that a finite-dimensional subspace of a normed linear space X is closed in X and use Baire's theorem.

The first important theorem about Banach spaces is

HEOREM 3.10 **Open Mapping Theorem**

Let X and Y be Banach spaces, $T \in \mathcal{B}(X, Y)$, and T surjective. Then T maps open sets onto open sets.

□ **PROOF**   Let B_r be the open ball of radius $r > 0$ in X. We first show that $\overline{T(B_r)}$ is a neighborhood of 0 in Y. Since T is surjective, it follows that $Y = \bigcup_{i=1}^{\infty} \overline{T(B_i)}$. Thus Baire's theorem implies that some $\overline{T(B_i)}$ has nonempty interior. Hence there exists $y_0 \in Y$ such that $y_0 \in \text{int}\,(\overline{T(B_i)})$ and $y_0 \in T(B_i)$ (int, of course, means interior). We now have

$$y_0 \in \text{int}\,(\overline{T(B_i)}) \iff 0 \in \text{int}\,(\overline{T(B_i)} - y_0).$$

Using Theorem 1.3a and the fact that $T(B_i) - y_0 \subseteq T(B_{2i})$, we obtain

$$\text{int}\,(\overline{T(B_i)} - y_0) = \text{int}\,(\overline{T(B_i) - y_0}) \subseteq \text{int}\,(\overline{T(B_{2i})}).$$

This shows that $\overline{T(B_{2i})}$ is a neighborhood of 0. Since T is homogeneous ($T(\alpha x) = \alpha Tx$) and nonzero scalar multiplication is a homeomorphism, $\overline{T(B_r)}$ is a neighborhood of 0 for every $r > 0$. In particular there exists an open ball $C_\epsilon = \{y \in Y : \|y\| < \epsilon\}$ such that $C_\epsilon \subseteq \overline{T(B_1)}$ and hence $C_{\epsilon \cdot 2^{-n}} \subseteq \overline{T(B_{2^{-n}})}$, $n = 1, 2, \ldots$. To show that T is an open map it now suffices to show that $0 \in \text{int}\,(T(B_r))$ for every $r > 0$. For then if U is open in X, and $y \in T(U)$ with $y = Tx$, we will have for some $r > 0$,

$$x + B_r \subseteq U \implies y + \text{int}\,(T(B_r)) \subseteq T(U),$$

so $T(U)$ will be open. Since $0 \in \text{int}\,(T(B_r)) \iff 0 \in \text{int}\,(T(B_3))$, the proof will be complete if we show that $C_\epsilon \subseteq T(B_3)$. Accordingly, let y be any member of C_ϵ. Since $C_\epsilon \subseteq \overline{T(B_1)}$, there exists

$$y_1 = Tx_1, \quad x_1 \in B_1, \quad \text{such that} \quad \|y_1 - y\| < \epsilon/2.$$

Since $C_{\epsilon/2} \subseteq \overline{T(B_{1/2})}$ we can now find

$$y_2 = Tx_2, \quad x_2 \in B_{1/2}, \quad \text{such that} \quad \|y - y_1 - y_2\| < \epsilon/4.$$

A straightforward induction argument shows that we can thus define a sequence $\{x_i\}_{i=1}^{\infty}$ with

$$y_i = Tx_i, \quad x_i \in B_{2^{-i+1}},$$

and

$$\|y - y_1 - y_2 - \cdots - y_i\| < \epsilon/2^i.$$

Defining $s_n = \sum_{i=1}^{n} x_i$, it is readily checked that $\{s_n\}_{n=1}^{\infty}$ is a Cauchy sequence in X and $\| s_n \| \leq \sum_{i=1}^{n} \| x_i \| < 2$. Since X is complete, there exists $x \in X$ such that $s_n \xrightarrow{\|\cdot\|} x$, and $\| x \| = \| \lim s_n \| \leq 2 < 3$. Finally, since T is continuous, Tx can also be determined by

$$Tx = T(\lim s_n) = \lim Ts_n = \lim (y_1 + y_2 + \cdots + y_n) = y.$$

Since $x \in B_3$, $y = Tx \in T(B_3)$. We have thus shown that $C_\epsilon \subseteq T(B_3)$, which completes the proof.

We have as an immediate consequence of this theorem the following

COROLLARY Let X and Y be Banach spaces and let $T \in \mathfrak{B}(X, Y)$ be bijective. Then T is a homeomorphism.

A second important and widely applied Banach space result uses this corollary in an ingenious way.

THEOREM 3.11

Closed Graph Theorem

Let X and Y be Banach spaces and let T be a linear transformation from X to Y. Then T is continuous $\Longleftrightarrow$ the graph of T is closed as a subset of $X \times Y$ endowed with the product topology.

□ **PROOF** We initially note that $X \times Y$ with the product topology is also a Banach space under (among others) the norm $\| (x,y) \| = \| x \| + \| y \|$. Addition and scalar multiplication are defined in the expected manner:

$$(x_1, y_1) + (x_2, y_2) = (x_1 + x_2, y_1 + y_2)$$

and

$$\alpha(x, y) = (\alpha x, \alpha y).$$

Completeness of $X \times Y$ follows easily.

$\Longrightarrow$: The graph G of T is defined by

$$G = \{(x, Tx) \in X \times Y : x \in X\}.$$

To show that G is closed in $X \times Y$ it is enough (by first countability) to show that G is sequentially closed. Accordingly, suppose $x_n \to x$ in X and $Tx_n \to y$ in Y. The continuity of T

implies that $Tx_n \to Tx$, and since Y is Hausdorff, we must have $y = Tx$. Thus $(x, y) \in G$ so G is closed in $X \times Y$.

$\Leftarrow$: Let P be the projection map from G onto X: $P(x, Tx) = x$. P is clearly a bijective continuous linear transformation from the normed linear space G to X. If G is closed, then B is a Banach space as a closed (and hence complete) subspace of $X \times Y$. Thus the corollary to the open mapping theorem yields that P is a homeomorphism. The continuity of P^{-1} says that $x_n \to x \Rightarrow Tx_n \to Tx$ and hence T is continuous.

EXERCISE 3.8   Let $(X_1, \| \ \|_1)$ and $(X_2, \| \ \|_2)$ be Banach spaces and let T be a linear transformation from X_1 to X_2. Suppose there exists a topology τ on X_2 such that:

(α) τ is a Hausdorff topology on X_2.
(β) τ is weaker than $\| \ \|_2$.
(γ) T is continuous from $(X_1, \| \ \|_1)$ to (X_2, τ).

Prove that $T : (X_1, \| \ \|_1) \to (X_2, \| \ \|_2)$ is continuous. Hint: Show that T has a closed graph by using (γ), (β), and (α) in that order.

The final member of our trio of widely acclaimed Banach space theorems is a statement about families of continuous linear transformations.

HEOREM 3.12   **Equicontinuity or Uniform Boundedness Principle**

Given a Banach space X, a normed linear space Y, and a family $\{T_\alpha\}_{\alpha \in I} \subseteq \mathcal{B}(X, Y)$, the following are equivalent:

a. $\{T_\alpha\}_{\alpha \in I}$ is an *equicontinuous* family, i.e., given $\epsilon > 0$ there exists $\delta > 0$ such that $\| x \| < \delta \Rightarrow \| T_\alpha x \| < \epsilon$ for all $\alpha \in I$.
b. For each $x \in X$, there exists $K_x \geq 0$ such that $\| T_\alpha x \| \leq K_x$ for all $\alpha \in I$.
c. There exists $K > 0$ such that $\| T_\alpha \| \leq K$ for all $\alpha \in I$, hence the $\{T_\alpha\}$ are *uniformly bounded*.

□   **PROOF**   (a) $\Rightarrow$ (b): By (a) we have that (taking $\epsilon = 1$) there exists $\delta > 0$ such that $\| x \| \leq \delta \Rightarrow \| T_\alpha x \| \leq 1$ for all $\alpha \in I$. Given any nonzero $x \in X$ we thus have $\| T_\alpha(\delta x / \| x \|) \| \leq 1$ for all $\alpha \in I$. It follows from this that $\| T_\alpha x \| \leq \| x \| / \delta = K_x$ for all $\alpha \in I$, establishing (b).

(b) $\implies$ (c): Define for each positive integer i the set

$$F_i = \{x \in X : \|T_\alpha x\| \le i \quad \text{for all} \quad \alpha \in I\}.$$

Each F_i is closed and, by (b), $X = \bigcup_{i=1}^{\infty} F_i$. Since X is complete, Baire's theorem ensures that some F_i must have nonempty interior. Thus F_i must contain some closed ball $\overline{B_r(x_0)}$ of radius $r > 0$ centered about some $x_0 \in F_i$. We then have

$$\sup\{\|T_\alpha x\| : x \in \overline{B_r(x_0)}\} \le i \qquad \text{for all} \quad \alpha \in I,$$

which implies that

$$\sup\{\|T_\alpha x\| : x \in \overline{(B_r(x_0)} - x_0)\} \le 2i \qquad \text{for all} \quad \alpha \in I$$

(where the fact that $\|Tx_0\| \le i$ and the triangle inequality have been used). Finally, noting that $r^{-1}\overline{(B_r(x_0)} - x_0) = \overline{B}_1$ (the closed unit ball), we have $\|T_\alpha\| = \sup_{x \in \overline{B}_1} \|T_\alpha x\| \le 2i/r = K$ for all $\alpha \in I$.

(c) $\implies$ (a): Given $\epsilon > 0$, choose $\delta = \epsilon/K$. Then $\|x\| < \delta \implies \|T_\alpha x\| \le K\|x\| < K \cdot \epsilon/K = \epsilon$ for all $\alpha \in I$, so $\{T_\alpha\}_{\alpha \in I}$ is equicontinuous.

COROLLARY A subset A of a normed linear space X is bounded $\iff$ $f(A)$ is bounded for every $f \in X^*$.

□ **PROOF** $\implies$: This is a consequence of Exercise 1.5b or Theorem 3.2e.

$\impliedby$: Consider the set $\hat{A} = \{\hat{x} \in X^{**} : x \in A\}$. For each $f \in X^*$,

$$\sup_{\hat{x} \in \hat{A}} |\hat{x}(f)| = \sup_{x \in A} |f(x)| < \infty.$$

Applying the uniform boundedness principle (b) $\implies$ (c) to $\hat{A}$ viewed as a family of continuous linear functionals on the Banach space X^*, we have $\sup_{\hat{x} \in \hat{A}} \|\hat{x}\| < \infty$. Since $\|\hat{x}\| = \|x\|$, we thus obtain $\sup_{x \in A} \|x\| < \infty$, so A is bounded in X.

EXERCISE 3.9 Let X be a Banach space, let Y be a normed linear space, and let $\{T_i\}_{i=1}^{\infty}$ be a sequence in $\mathcal{B}(X, Y)$ with the property that $Tx = \lim_{i \to \infty} T_i x$ exists for all $x \in X$. Prove that $T \in \mathcal{B}(X, Y)$.

□   THE ADJOINT OF A CONTINUOUS
LINEAR TRANSFORMATION

Given normed linear spaces X and Y and given $T \in \mathcal{B}(X, Y)$, we define the *adjoint* T^* of T as follows: $T^*: Y^* \to X^*$ where

$$T^*g = g \circ T \quad \text{or} \quad (T^*g)x = g(Tx), \quad g \in Y^*, \quad x \in X.$$

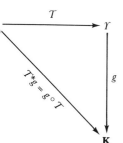

T

Y

g

$T^*g = g \circ T$

K   FIGURE 3.1

THEOREM 3.13   Given X and Y normed linear spaces and $T \in \mathcal{B}(X, Y)$:

(a) $T^* \in \mathcal{B}(Y^*, X^*)$.
(b) $\|T^*\| = \|T\|$.
(c) The mapping $*: \mathcal{B}(X, Y) \to \mathcal{B}(Y^*, X^*)$ is linear, injective, and an isometry.

□   **PROOF**   (a) T^* is linear since

$$\begin{aligned}
(T^*(\alpha_1 g_1 + \alpha_2 g_2))x &= (\alpha_1 g_1 + \alpha_2 g_2)(Tx) \\
&= \alpha_1 g_1(Tx) + \alpha_2 g_2(Tx) \\
&= \alpha_1(T^*g_1)x + \alpha_2(T^*g_2)x \\
&= (\alpha_1 T^*g_1 + \alpha_2 T^*g_2)x.
\end{aligned}$$

Also,

$$\begin{aligned}
\|T^*\| &= \sup_{\|g\| \le 1} \|T^*g\| = \sup_{\substack{\|g\| \le 1 \\ \|x\| \le 1}} |(T^*g)x| = \sup_{\substack{\|g\| \le 1 \\ \|x\| \le 1}} |g(Tx)| \\
&\le \sup_{\|x\| \le 1} \|Tx\| \quad (\text{since } \|g\| \le 1) \\
&= \|T\|.
\end{aligned} \tag{1}$$

Hence T^* is bounded and we have shown that $T \in \mathcal{B}\,(Y^*,X^*)$.

(b) An application of the corollary to the Hahn–Banach theorem (3.5) to any nonzero $Tx \in Y$ yields $g \in Y^*$, $\|g\| = 1$, such that $|g(Tx)| = \|Tx\|$. Hence the one inequality in (1) above is in fact an equality, so $\|T^*\| = \|T\|$.

(c)

$$
\begin{aligned}
((\alpha_1 T_1 + \alpha_2 T_2)^* g)\, x &= g((\alpha_1 T_1 + \alpha_2 T_2)x) \\
&= g(\alpha_1 T_1 x + \alpha_2 T_2 x) \\
&= \alpha_1 g(T_1 x) + \alpha_2 g(T_2 x) \\
&= \alpha_1 (T_1^* g)x + \alpha_2 (T_2^* g)x \\
&= (\alpha_1 (T_1^* g) + \alpha_2 (T_2^* g))x \\
&= ((\alpha_1 T_1^* + \alpha_2 T_2^*)g)x.
\end{aligned}
$$

Since $(\alpha_1 T_1 + \alpha_2 T_2)^*$ and $\alpha_1 T_1^* + \alpha_2 T_2^*$ applied to $g \in Y^*$ yield the same result as is indicated by their identical values on x, the two are equal and $*$ is linear. We have shown in (b) that $*$ is an isometry, and it is an easy exercise to show that a linear isometry must be injective.

EXERCISE 3.10 Let $T \in \mathcal{B}(X,Y)$ and $S \in \mathcal{B}(Y,Z)$ where X, Y, and Z are normed linear spaces. Accepting the familiar result that a composition of continuous linear transformations is continuous and linear argue that $(S \circ T)^* = T^* \circ S^*$.

If we take $Y = X$, then $\mathcal{B}(X) = \mathcal{B}(X,X)$ becomes an *algebra* under composition, i.e., $\mathcal{B}(X)$ has defined on it a "multiplication" that fits in well with the linear space addition and scalar multiplication (see Chapter 6 for details). The word transformation is then often specialized to the word *operator*. In this context, the results of Theorem 3.13 and Exercise 3.10 show that the adjoint mapping shares many of the properties of complex conjugation acting on the linear space $\mathbf{C}$, which may be identified with $\mathcal{B}\,(\mathbf{C})$. (In fact the word *conjugate* is often used where we have used *adjoint*.) The generalization of the complex conjugate to the adjoint mapping would be an ideal one if we restricted ourselves to Banach spaces X for which X and X^* were (isometrically) identifiable with each other. In this case we might identify $\mathcal{B}\,(X)$ and $\mathcal{B}(X^*)$, we could regard $T^* \in \mathcal{B}\,(X)$ for any $T \in \mathcal{B}\,(X)$, and in fact we would have $T^{**} = T$. This is one of the many reasons our next specialization will focus upon Hilbert space, where this property of self-conjugacy is present.

Before we take up this study we present an abstract development of integration theory which, in addition to its independent importance, will serve to establish many of the facts that we have asserted about L^p spaces.

□ REMARKS

An intermediate notion to those of a locally convex space and of a normed linear space is that of a locally convex space whose topology is determined by a translation invariant metric. Such a space that is, in addition, complete is called a *Frechet space*. Since the use of the completeness hypothesis in many of the theorems of this chapter was based on Baire's theorem or some other norm-independent property, it is natural to expect a generalization of much of the theory to Frechet spaces. Such generalization is possible and often fruitful [7, Chapter II].

The literature is rich with generalizations and applications of the open mapping, closed graph, and uniform boundedness theorems. See Dunford and Schwartz's book, [2, pp. 80–85] for some (often fairly specialized) references to these three theorems. As is evident from its proof, the main content of the uniform boundedness principle is (b) $\Longrightarrow$ (c). This is often stated in contrapositive form not (c) $\Longrightarrow$ not (b) and is sometimes called the Banach–Steinhaus theorem. For a pleasing application of the uniform boundedness principle to the theory of Fourier series, see an article by Goffman and Waterman [10].

The coincidence in a Banach space setting of the linear transformations with closed graphs and the continuous linear transformations suggests a fruitful alternative to continuity in more general settings where the notions do not coincide. We shall employ this alternative in Chapter 5 when discussing unbounded operators on Hilbert space (the differentiation operator on many function spaces has closed graph but is not continuous—no contradiction since it is not everywhere defined). Functions with closed graphs also provide a means for stating for non-Hausdorff spaces theorems that may fail for continuous functions. (See Wilansky's article [11] entitled "Life without T_2.")

The problem of finding a concrete representation for the conjugate space X^* of a normed linear space X is one that we have so far examined only for $X = l^1$ (and in Problem 2 following, $X = c_0$). For an exceedingly thorough investigation of the conjugate spaces and other properties of 28 different kinds of Banach spaces, see again Danford and Schwartz's book [9, Chapter IV and the table of special spaces at the end of that chapter (starting p. 374)].

The definition of the adjoint transformation and the study of transformations between spaces can be carried out in considerably more generality than we have done in our restriction to normed linear and Banach spaces. As might be expected, the presence of norms facilitates this study greatly (witness $\| T \| = \| T^* \|$). Yosida's book [7] extends a great deal of the theory of Banach spaces to sequentially complete locally convex spaces. This theory then covers such important spaces as $\mathcal{Q}(D)$ and $\mathcal{D}(\mathbf{R}^n)$.

□ **PROBLEMS**

1. a. Let M be a closed subspace of a normed linear space X. Compute the norm of the quotient mapping $Q: X \to X/M$ regarded as a linear transformation between normed linear spaces.

   b. Given the Banach space $\mathcal{C}([0, 1])$ (sup norm) and $M = \{ f \in \mathcal{C}([0, 1]) : f(\tfrac{1}{2}) = 0 \}$, argue that $\mathcal{C}([0, 1])/M$ is a Banach space. What is the dimension of $\mathcal{C}([0, 1])/M$ and what is an explicit description of the norm on $\mathcal{C}([0, 1])/M$?

2. Let c_0 denote the subspace of l^∞ consisting of all $\mathbf{K}$-valued sequences that are convergent to 0.

   a. Recalling our approach to proving that $(l^1)^* \cong l^\infty$, prove that $(c_0)^* \cong l^1$. Hint: The proof that $t' \in (c_0)^* \Rightarrow t \in l^1$ requires some care.

   b. Recalling that X is defined to be separable if it has a countable dense subset, argue that c_0 is separable and l^∞ is not. Hints: To show that c_0 is separable consider the set of all sequences whose terms are rational (or have rational real and imaginary parts) and eventually 0. To show that l^∞ is not separable consider the set of all sequences whose terms contain only ones and zeros. What is the cardinality of this set and how far apart in the l^∞ norm must unequal members be?

   c. Conclude that c_0 is a nonreflexive normed linear space.

3. Let X be a normed linear space. Prove that the weak* topology coincides with the strong (normed) topology on $X^* \Leftrightarrow X$ is finite dimensional. Hint for $\Leftarrow$: As a result of Problem 5, Chapter 1, you may assume $X = \mathbf{K}^n$ endowed with some friendly norm.

4. Given a linear space X and (norm induced) topologies τ_1 and τ_2 on X such that (X, τ_1) and (X, τ_2) are Banach spaces, prove that if $(X, \tau_1 \cap \tau_2)$ is a Banach space, then $\tau_1 = \tau_2$. This shows in particular that if τ_1 and τ_2 are comparable (one collection of open sets is a subcollection of the other), they must coincide. (Recall that $\tau_1 \cap \tau_2$ is the intersection of the topologies τ_1 and τ_2.)

5. a. Define $f: \mathbf{R} \to \mathbf{R}$ by
$$f(x) = \begin{cases} 1/x, & x \neq 0 \\ 0, & x = 0. \end{cases}$$
Argue that the graph of f is closed (as a subset of $\mathbf{R} \times \mathbf{R}$) but that f is not continuous. Why does this result not contradict the closed graph theorem?

b. Prove for any topological space S and any Hausdorff space T that $f: S \to T$ continuous $\Rightarrow f$ has a sequentially closed graph.

c. What can go wrong in (b) above if T is not Hausdorff?

6. Prove that a closed, balanced convex subset U of a Banach space X is a neighborhood of $0 \Leftrightarrow U$ is absorbing. Hint for $\Leftarrow$: Show that U has nonempty interior and then use convexity to show $0 \in \mathrm{int}\,(U)$.

7. *Operator topologies:* Given normed linear spaces X and Y there are many ways to topologize $\mathfrak{B}(X, Y)$ as a tls. We consider three of them.

Uniform operator topology: the topology on $\mathfrak{B}(X, Y)$ induced by $\|\ \|$. Thus $T_n \xrightarrow{\|\ \|} 0$ if and only if $\|T_n\| \to 0$.

Strong operator topology: the weakest topology on $\mathfrak{B}(X, Y)$ such that, for every $x \in X$, $\hat{x}: \mathfrak{B}(X, Y) \to Y$ is continuous, where $\hat{x}(T) = Tx$. Thus $T_n \xrightarrow{\text{strong}} 0$ if and only if $\|T_n x\| \to 0$ for all $x \in X$.

Weak operator topology: the weakest topology on $\mathfrak{B}(X, Y)$ such that for each $x \in X$ and $g \in Y^*$, $L_{x,g}: \mathfrak{B}(X, Y) \to \mathbf{K}$ is continuous, where $L_{x,g}(T) = g(Tx)$. Thus $T_n \xrightarrow{\text{weak}} 0$ if and only if $g(T_n x) \to 0$ in $\mathbf{K}$ for all $x \in X$ and $g \in Y^*$.

a. Sketch proofs that each of these topologies makes $\mathcal{B}(X,Y)$ into a locally convex space.

b. Prove that the weak operator topology is weaker than the strong operator topology which is in turn weaker than the uniform operator topology.

c. Let $Y = X$ and define $M : \mathcal{B}(X) \times \mathcal{B}(X) \rightarrow \mathcal{B}(X)$ by $M(S,T) = S \circ T$ (henceforth just ST). Prove that if $\mathcal{B}(X)$ is given its uniform operator topology the multiplication operation M is continuous.

d. Let $X = l^1$ and define the shift operators S and $T \in \mathcal{B}(X)$ by $S(x_1, x_2, \ldots) = (x_2, x_3, \ldots)$ and $T(x_1, x_2, \ldots) = (0, x_1, x_2, \ldots)$. Let $S^n = S \circ S \circ \cdots \circ S$ (n times) and similarly for T^n. Prove that $S^n \rightarrow 0$ and $T^n \rightarrow 0$ (as in $n \rightarrow \infty$) in the weak operator topology but not in the strong or uniform operator topologies. Then show that $S^n T^n \nrightarrow 0$ in the weak operator topology, so M (from c) is not continuous in this topology. Finally, show that $T^n S^n \rightarrow 0$ in the strong (and hence weak) operator topology but not in the uniform operator topology.

8. Let X be a Banach space and let $\mathcal{F}$ be a family of operators in $\mathcal{B}(X)$.

a. Argue that $\mathcal{F}$ is bounded in the weak operator topology on $\mathcal{B}(X)$ if and only if for each $x \in X$ and $g \in X^*$ there exists $M \geq 0$ (depending on x and g) such that $\| g(Tx) \| \leq M$ for all $T \in \mathcal{F}$.

b. Prove that if $\mathcal{F}$ is bounded in the weak operator topology, then there exists $N > 0$ such that $\| T \| \leq N$ for all $T \in \mathcal{F}$, so that $\mathcal{F}$ is bounded in the uniform operator topology. Hints: Fix $x \in X$, $\| x \| \leq 1$, and apply the uniform boundedness principle to the family $\{ \widehat{Tx} \in X^{**} : T \in \mathcal{F} \}$.

9. Let the normed linear space X be reflexive and let $T \in \mathcal{B}(X)$. By identifying X and X^{**}, prove that $T \text{ "} = \text{" } T^{**}$. Hint: For each $x \in X$ show that $T^{**} \hat{x} = \widehat{Tx}$ by adeptly using definitions of the $\wedge$ and $*$ mappings.

Integration and Measure

4

□ **AN OVERVIEW**

In this chapter we present a procedure for extending certain kinds of linear functionals, called integrals, on function spaces to integrals on larger classes of functions. The procedure, when carried out on spaces of functions defined on an arbitrary set S, results in the *Daniell integral*, and the special case where $S \subseteq \mathbf{R}^n$ will provide the extension from the Riemann integral to the Lebesgue integral. The reader who has not seen a development of the Lebesque integral on $\mathbf{R}$ would do well to keep in mind throughout our development the case where $S \subseteq \mathbf{R}$. When the fog clears, it will be seen that the arguments remain unchanged for the general case of an abstract set. Direct consequences of our approach are generalizations of some of the classical integration theorems on convergence and the vital correspondence between integrals and measures.

We are then able to define, in a general setting, the L^p spaces referred to in the preceding chapter, establishing that they are Banach spaces. Finally, after proving a few of the deeper results of integration theory, we are able to establish the concrete representation of the conjugate space of an L^p space mentioned in Chapter 3.

□ **INTEGRALS ON LINEAR LATTICES OF FUNCTIONS**

A *linear lattice of functions* $\mathcal{L}$ on a set S is a linear space of real-valued functions on S such that $\mathcal{L}$ is closed under the lattice operations $\vee$ and $\wedge$, where

$$f \vee g: S \to \mathbf{R}, \quad f \vee g(x) = \max\{f(x), g(x)\}$$
$$f \wedge g: S \to \mathbf{R}, \quad f \wedge g(x) = \min\{f(x), g(x)\}.$$

It follows immediately that $|f| \in \mathcal{L}$ since $|f| = f \vee 0 - f \wedge 0$ (or try $|f| = f \vee (-f)$).

Given $\{f_i\}_{i=1}^{\infty}$ and f in $\mathcal{L}$ we introduce the notation $f_i \downarrow f$ to mean $f_i(x)$ converges in monotone decreasing fashion to $f(x)$ for every $x \in S$ (and similarly of course for $f_i \uparrow f$).

We define an *integral* on $\mathcal{L}$ to be a function $I: \mathcal{L} \to \mathbf{R}$ that satisfies for all $f, g \in \mathcal{L}$ and $\alpha \in \mathbf{R}$:

(1) $I(f + g) = I(f) + I(g)$ (I is *additive*).
(2) $I(\alpha f) = \alpha I(f)$ (I is *homogeneous*).
(3) $f \geq 0 \Rightarrow I(f) \geq 0$ (I is *nonnegative* on nonnegative functions).

(4) $\{f_i\}_{i=1}^{\infty}$ in $\mathcal{L}$ and
    $f_i \downarrow 0 \Rightarrow I(f_i) \downarrow 0$ (I is *monotone continuous*).

EXERCISE 4.1   Prove that, in the presence of (1) and (2), (3) and (4) are respectively equivalent to

(3') $f \geq g \Rightarrow I(f) \geq I(g)$.
(4') $\{f_i\}_{i=1}^{\infty}$ and f in $\mathcal{L}$ and $f_i \uparrow f \Rightarrow I(f_i) \uparrow I(f)$ and similarly for $f_i \downarrow f$.

An integral I on $\mathcal{L}$ is clearly a linear functional, and somewhat in the spirit of the Hahn–Banach theorem we would like to extend I to an integral (which we still call I) on a more inclusive linear lattice $\mathcal{L}^1$ of functions on S. The current emphasis as well as the historical origin of this extension procedure centers around $\mathcal{L}^1$ being closed with respect to certain limit-type operations and I satisfying "continuity" with respect to these operations.

The following exercise shows that the Riemann integral provides an example of the concepts we have defined. The exercise also shows the incomplete nature of the Riemann integral and motivates the need for extending it as mentioned in the previous paragraph.

EXERCISE 4.2   Let $S = [0, 1]$, $\mathcal{L} = \mathcal{C}([0, 1])$ (real-valued), and let I be the ordinary Riemann integral on $\mathcal{L}$.

a. Prove that the Riemann integral is indeed an integral on $\mathcal{C}([0, 1])$. You may accept properties (1), (2), and (3) as well known. Hint for (4): Use the compactness of $[0, 1]$ to show that $f_i \downarrow 0 \Rightarrow f_i \xrightarrow{\text{uniformly}} 0$.

b. Show that $\{f_i\}_{i=1}^{\infty} \in \mathcal{C}([0, 1])$ and $f_i \downarrow f$ does not imply that $f \in \mathcal{C}([0, 1])$. Thus $\mathcal{L}$ (and hence I) does not preserve limit operations.

c. If we replace $\mathcal{C}([0, 1])$ by the larger class $\mathcal{R}$ of all Riemann integrable functions on $[0, 1]$, it is true (there appears to be no easy direct proof) that the Riemann integral is again an integral on $\mathcal{R}$. Show that even $\mathcal{R}$ is not closed under monotone limits, i.e., repeat (b) with $\mathcal{C}([0, 1])$ replaced by $\mathcal{R}$. Hint: By enumerating the rationals, choose a sequence that decreases monotonically to

$$f: [0, 1] \to \mathbf{R}, \qquad f(x) = \begin{cases} 1, & x \text{ irrational} \\ 0, & x \text{ rational.} \end{cases}$$

☐ **BAIRE FUNCTIONS AND THE EXTENSION PROCEDURE**

We define a monotone family of real-valued functions on a set S as one that is closed under the operation of taking monotone increasing and decreasing limits (i.e., if $\{f_i\}_{i=1}^{\infty}$ are in the family and $f_i \uparrow f$, then f is also).

Given a linear lattice $\mathcal{L}$ of functions on S, the *Baire functions* $\mathcal{B}$ on S are defined to be the smallest monotone family (of real-valued functions on S) containing $\mathcal{L}$. Since the collection of all functions on S provides an example of a monotone family containing $\mathcal{L}$, and since an intersection of monotone families is monotone, $\mathcal{B}$ is a well-defined family which includes $\mathcal{L}$.

THEOREM 4.1   Let $\mathcal{L}$ be any linear lattice of functions and $\mathcal{B}$ its extension to the Baire functions. Then $\mathcal{B}$ is also a linear lattice.

☐ **PROOF**   We first show that $\mathcal{B}$ is closed under scalar (real) multiplication. Define

$$M = \{f \in \mathcal{B} : \alpha f \in \mathcal{B} \quad \text{for all} \quad \alpha \in \mathbf{R}\}.$$

Then M is readily seen to be monotone and to include $\mathcal{L}$. Since M is a monotone family containing $\mathcal{L}$ and $M \subseteq \mathcal{B}$, the definition of $\mathcal{B}$ yields $M = \mathcal{B}$. Hence $\mathcal{B}$ is closed under scalar multiplication since M is. For closure under the three binary operations of $+, \vee$, and $\wedge$, define for each $f \in \mathcal{B}$,

$$M(f) = \{g \in \mathcal{B} : f + g, \quad f \vee g, \quad \text{and} \quad f \wedge g \in \mathcal{B}\}.$$

Then $M(f)$ is easily seen to be monotone. For instance,

$\{g_i\}_{i=1}^{\infty}$ in $M(f)$ and

$$g_i \uparrow g \implies \{f \vee g_i\} \text{ in } \mathcal{B} \quad \text{and} \quad (f \vee g_i) \uparrow f \vee g$$
$$\implies f \vee g \in \mathcal{B}.$$

Given $f \in \mathcal{L}$ we have $\mathcal{L} \subseteq M(f)$ so, as reasoned above, $M(f) = \mathcal{B}$. Now given any $g \in \mathcal{B}$ we have

$$f \in \mathcal{L} \implies g \in M(f) \qquad \text{(since } M(f) = \mathcal{B}\text{)}$$
$$\implies f \in M(g) \qquad \text{(definition of } M(f) \text{ and } M(g)\text{),}$$

so that $\mathcal{L} \subseteq M(g)$. We conclude that $M(g) = \mathcal{B}$ for all $g \in \mathcal{B}$, which says directly that $\mathcal{B}$ is closed with respect to $+, \vee$, and $\wedge$.

Our next goal is to show how any integral I on $\mathcal{L}$ can be extended to an integral on a larger class of functions. In order to do this we introduce the *extended real numbers* $\mathbf{R}^e$, where $\mathbf{R}^e = \mathbf{R} \cup \{\infty\} \cup \{-\infty\}$. Operations on $\mathbf{R}^e$ involving ∞ and $-\infty$ are defined as would be expected, including

$$0 \cdot (\pm \infty) = (\pm \infty) \cdot 0 = 0,$$
$$(\infty + (-\infty), \; -\infty + \infty \quad \text{undefined}).$$

In extending the real numbers in this fashion we are sacrificing many of the algebraic properties of $\mathbf{R}$ (for instance $\mathbf{R}^e$ is no longer a group), but the extension is more or less forced upon us by measure theoretic conventions (where for instance the real line is regarded as a Lebesgue measurable set with measure ∞ and real-valued functions need not be defined at all points in their supposed domains). A useful property of $\mathbf{R}^e$ for our purposes is that every increasing (or decreasing) sequence in $\mathbf{R}^e$ converges to a member of $\mathbf{R}^e$ (i.e., we regard an increasing and unbounded sequence as converging to ∞). All this can be made topologically precise (via a two-point compactification of $\mathbf{R}$), but there is no real need to do so for what follows.

Given a linear lattice of functions $\mathcal{L}$ on a set S we now define $\overline{B} = \{f: S \to \mathbf{R}^e : \text{there exists } \{f_i\}_{i=1}^{\infty} \text{ in } \mathcal{L} \text{ such that } f_i \uparrow f\}$ and $\underline{B} = \{f: S \to \mathbf{R}^e : \text{there exists } \{f_i\}_{i=1}^{\infty} \text{ in } \mathcal{L} \text{ such that } f_i \downarrow f\}$. While $\overline{B}$ and $\underline{B}$ are not subsets of $\mathcal{B}$, it is easy to see that any $f \in \overline{B}$ or $\underline{B}$ which takes values only in $\mathbf{R}$ must belong to $\mathcal{B}$, but that members of $\mathcal{B}$ certainly need not be in $\overline{B}$ or $\underline{B}$.

Clearly $\overline{B}$ and $\underline{B}$ include $\mathcal{L}$ since any $f \in \mathcal{L}$ is a monotone limit of the constant sequence all of whose terms are f. Given any integral I on $\mathcal{L}$, we now propose to extend I to an $\mathbf{R}^e$-valued function $\bar{I}$ on $\bar{B}$ as follows: Given $f \in \bar{B}$ obtain a sequence $\{f_i\}_{i=1}^{\infty}$ in $\mathcal{L}$ with $f_i \uparrow f$ and let

$$\bar{I}(f) = \lim I(f_i).$$

An analogous proposal is made for defining $\underline{I}$ on $\underline{B}$. We must show that this procedure provides a valid way for defining $\bar{I}$ and $\underline{I}$ in the sense that the definitions are independent of how the monotone sequence $\{f_i\}_{i=1}^{\infty}$ is chosen from $\mathcal{L}$.

LEMMA 4.2   Given an integral I on a linear lattice $\mathcal{L}$ of functions:

a. $\bar{I}$ and $\underline{I}$ are well defined on $\bar{B}$ and $\underline{B}$ respectively, and both extend I on $\mathcal{L}$.
b. $\bar{I}$ and $\underline{I}$ are nonnegative on nonnegative functions.
c. $\{f_i\}_{i=1}^{\infty}$ in $\bar{B}$ and $f_i \uparrow f \Rightarrow f \in \bar{B}$ and $\bar{I}(f_i) \uparrow \bar{I}(f)$, and analogously for $\underline{B}$ and $\underline{I}$.

□ **PROOF**   We carry out proofs for $\bar{B}$ and $\bar{I}$; the proofs for $\underline{B}$ and $\underline{I}$ are virtually identical. We do (a) and (b) together as follows: Suppose $\{f_i\}_{i=1}^{\infty}$ and $\{g_j\}_{j=1}^{\infty}$ are increasing sequences in L such that $f_i \uparrow f$ and $g_j \uparrow g$ and $g \leq f$. It will be shown that

$$\lim I(f_i) \geq \lim I(g_j). \qquad (1)$$

Note that these limits, taken in $\mathbf{R}^e$, always exist. This will establish (a) by taking $f = g$ and reversing the roles of f_i and g_j in (1). With $\bar{I}$ well defined, (b) then follows since

$$\bar{I}(f) = \lim I(f_i) \geq \lim I(g_j) = \bar{I}(g).$$

To establish (1) we first observe that if $k \in \mathcal{L}$ and $\lim f_i \geq k$ then $f_i \geq f_i \wedge k$ and $(f_i \wedge k) \uparrow k$. By properties of I on $\mathcal{L}$ we then have

$$\lim I(f_i) \geq \lim I(f_i \wedge k) = I(k).$$

Choosing $k = g_j$ and taking limits as $j \to \infty$, we obtain (1); so $\bar{I}$ is well defined and nonnegative. Finally, $\bar{I}$ agrees with I for $f \in \mathcal{L}$ since $\bar{I}(f) = \lim I(f) = I(f)$.

(c) Given $\{f_i\}_{i=1}^{\infty}$ in $\bar{B}$ and $f_i \uparrow f$, choose for each i a sequence

$\{g_i^k\}_{k=1}^\infty$ from $\mathcal{L}$ with $g_i^k \uparrow_k f_i$. Define

$$h_i = g_1^i \vee g_2^i \vee \cdots \vee g_i^i.$$

Then $\{h_i\}_{i=1}^\infty$ is a monotone increasing sequence in $\mathcal{L}$ and

$$g_j^i \leq h_i \leq f_i \qquad \text{for all} \quad j \leq i.$$

Taking limits first with respect to i and then with respect to j we obtain $f \leq \lim h_i \leq f$, so $h_i \uparrow f$ and hence $f \in \bar{B}$. Taking limits in a similar fashion with the inequalities

$$I(g_j^i) \leq I(h_i) \leq \bar{I}(f_i)$$

we obtain

$$\lim \bar{I}(f_j) \leq \bar{I}(f) \leq \lim \bar{I}(f_i),$$

so $\bar{I}(f_i) \uparrow \bar{I}(f)$.

LEMMA 4.3   (a) $f, g \in \bar{B} \implies f + g \in \bar{B}$ and $\bar{I}(f + g) = \bar{I}(f) + \bar{I}(g)$ and similarly for $\underline{B}$ and $\underline{I}$.

(b) $f \in \bar{B}$ and $\alpha \geq 0 \implies \alpha f \in \bar{B}$ and $\bar{I}(\alpha f) = \alpha \bar{I}(f)$ and similarly for $\underline{B}$ and $\underline{I}$.

(c) $\bar{B}$ and $\underline{B}$ are closed under $\vee$ and $\wedge$.

(d) $f \in \underline{B} \iff -f \in \bar{B}$; and $f \in \underline{B} \implies \underline{I}(f) = -\bar{I}(-f)$.

(e) $\bar{f} \in \bar{B}, \underline{f} \in \underline{B}$ and $\underline{f} \leq \bar{f} \implies \bar{f} - \underline{f} \in \bar{B}$ and $\bar{I}(\bar{f}) - \underline{I}(\underline{f}) \geq 0$.

□ **PROOF**   (a) Choose $\{f_i\}_{i=1}^\infty$ and $\{g_i\}_{i=1}^\infty$ in $\mathcal{L}$ so that $f_i \uparrow f$ and $g_i \uparrow g$. Then $(f_i + g_i) \uparrow f + g$, so $f + g \in \bar{B}$, and

$$\bar{I}(f + g) = \lim I(f_i + g_i) = \lim I(f_i) + \lim I(g_i) = \bar{I}(f) + \bar{I}(g).$$

The proof for $\underline{B}$ and $\underline{I}$ is, of course, very similar.

(b) and (c)   These proofs are very similar to that of (a) and will be omitted. The reader should be sure to see why we restrict to $\alpha \geq 0$ in (b).

(d) $f \in \underline{B} \iff$ there exists $\{f_i\}_{i=1}^\infty$ in $\mathcal{L}$ with $f_i \downarrow f$

$\iff$ there exists $\{-f_i\}_{i=1}^\infty$ in $\mathcal{L}$ with $(-f_i) \uparrow -f$

$\iff -f \in \bar{B}$.

Also, $\underline{I}(f) = \lim I(f_i) = -\lim I(-f_i) = -\bar{I}(-f)$.

(e) By (a) and (d), $\bar{f} - \underline{f} = \bar{f} + (-\underline{f}) \in \bar{B}$ and

$$\bar{I}(\bar{f}) - \underline{I}(\underline{f}) = \bar{I}(\bar{f}) + \bar{I}(-\underline{f}) = \bar{I}(\bar{f} - \underline{f}) \geq 0.$$

We are now prepared to make the key definitions and to develop the main theorem of the extension procedure. Let it be assumed in what follows that $\underline{f} \in \underline{B}$ and $\bar{f} \in \bar{B}$. We define the space $\mathcal{L}^1$ of *summable functions* by

$$\mathcal{L}^1 = \{f \in \mathcal{B} : -\infty < \sup_{\underline{f} \leq f} \underline{I}(\underline{f}) = \inf_{\bar{f} \geq f} \bar{I}(\bar{f}) < \infty\}.$$

Equivalently, a Baire function f is in $\mathcal{L}^1$ provided that for each $\epsilon > 0$ there exist $\underline{f} \in \underline{B}$ and $\bar{f} \in \bar{B}$ such that $\underline{f} \leq f \leq \bar{f}$ and $\bar{I}(\bar{f}) - \underline{I}(\underline{f}) < \epsilon$. Note that $\bar{I}(\bar{f}) - \underline{I}(\underline{f}) \geq 0$ by Lemma 4.3e.

Given $f \in \mathcal{L}^1$ we define

$$I(f) = \sup_{\underline{f} \leq f} \underline{I}(\underline{f}) = \inf_{\bar{f} \geq f} \bar{I}(\bar{f}).$$

The multiple use of I should cause no problem in view of the following exercise.

EXERCISE 4.3 a. Prove that $\mathcal{L}^1$ contains $\mathcal{L}$ and that I as defined above on $\mathcal{L}^1$ agrees with the old integral I on $\mathcal{L}$.

b. Prove that $f \in \bar{B} \cap \mathcal{B}$ and $\bar{I}(f) < \infty \Longrightarrow f \in \mathcal{L}^1$ and $I(f) = \bar{I}(f)$. A similar result holds for $f \in \underline{B} \cap \mathcal{B}$.

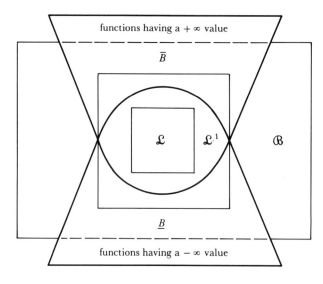

functions having a $+\infty$ value

$\bar{B}$

$\mathcal{L}$ $\mathcal{L}^1$ $\mathcal{B}$

$\underline{B}$

functions having a $-\infty$ value

FIGURE 4.1

Figure 4.1 summarizes diagrammatically the various extensions of $\mathcal{L}$ that we have used to obtain $\mathcal{L}^1$. Anticipating the following theorem, we have drawn the extensions that are linear lattices as rectangles and those with integrals defined on them as squares.

THEOREM 4.4 $\mathcal{L}^1$ is a linear lattice of functions on S and I satisfies the defining properties (1)–(4) of an integral on $\mathcal{L}^1$.

□ **PROOF** Lattice properties, closure under addition, and (1): Given $f_1, f_2 \in \mathcal{L}^1$ and $\epsilon > 0$, choose $\underline{f_1}, \underline{f_2} \in \underline{B}$ and $\overline{f_1}, \overline{f_2} \in \overline{B}$ such that $\underline{f_i} \leq f_i \leq \overline{f_i}$ and

$$\overline{I}(\overline{f_i}) - \underline{I}(\underline{f_i}) < \epsilon/4, \qquad i = 1, 2.$$

Letting $\triangle$ denote any of the operations $+, \vee, \wedge$, we have

$$\underline{f_1} \triangle \underline{f_2} \leq f_1 \triangle f_2 \leq \overline{f_1} \triangle \overline{f_2}$$

and

$$\overline{f_1} \triangle \overline{f_2} - \underline{f_1} \triangle \underline{f_2} \leq (\overline{f_1} - \underline{f_1}) + (\overline{f_2} - \underline{f_2}),$$

where the latter inequality is obvious for $\triangle = +$, but needs case by case verification for $\vee$ and $\wedge$ (we omit the details). Thus,

$$\overline{I}(\overline{f_1} \triangle \overline{f_2}) - \underline{I}(\underline{f_1} \triangle \underline{f_2}) \leq \overline{I}(\overline{f_1}) - \underline{I}(\underline{f_1}) + \overline{I}(\overline{f_2}) - \underline{I}(\underline{f_2}) < \epsilon/2,$$

so $f_1 + f_2, f_1 \vee f_2$, and $f_1 \wedge f_2$ are in $\mathcal{L}^1$. Furthermore,

$$\begin{aligned}
-\epsilon < \; & (\underline{I}(\underline{f_1}) - I(f_1)) + (\underline{I}(\underline{f_2}) - I(f_2)) \\
& - (\underline{I}(\underline{f_1} + \underline{f_2}) - I(f_1 + f_2)) \\
= \; & I(f_1 + f_2) - I(f_1) - I(f_2) \\
= \; & (\overline{I}(\overline{f_1}) - I(f_1)) + (\overline{I}(\overline{f_2}) - I(f_2)) \\
& - (\overline{I}(\overline{f_1} + \overline{f_2}) - I(f_1 + f_2)) < \epsilon,
\end{aligned}$$

where additivity of $\underline{I}$ on $\underline{B}$ and of $\overline{I}$ on $\overline{B}$ have been used. We thus have

$$| I(f_1 + f_2) - I(f_1) - I(f_2) | < \epsilon;$$

since $\epsilon > 0$ was arbitrary, we conclude that I is additive on $\mathcal{L}^1$.

Closure under scalar multiplication and (2): $f \in \mathcal{L}^1 \implies \alpha f \in \mathcal{L}^1$ is straightforward if $\alpha \geq 0$, as is $I(\alpha f) = \alpha I(f)$. If $\alpha < 0$, let $\epsilon > 0$ be given and choose $\underline{f} \in \underline{B}, \overline{f} \in \overline{B}$ such that $\underline{f} \leq f \leq \overline{f}$ and

$\bar{I}(\bar{f}) - \underline{I}(\underline{f}) < \epsilon/-\alpha$. Then $\alpha\bar{f} \in \underline{B}$, $\alpha\underline{f} \in \bar{B}$, and $\alpha\bar{f} \leq \alpha f \leq \alpha\underline{f}$. Furthermore,

$$\bar{I}(\alpha\underline{f}) - \underline{I}(\alpha\bar{f}) = (-\alpha)\bar{I}(-f) + \alpha\underline{I}(-\bar{f})$$
$$= \alpha\underline{I}(\underline{f}) - \alpha\bar{I}(\bar{f})$$
$$= -\alpha(\bar{I}(\bar{f}) - \underline{I}(\underline{f})) < \epsilon.$$

Hence $\alpha f \in \mathcal{L}^1$ and an argument similar to that of the preceding paragraph uses the nonnegative homogeneity of $\underline{I}$ and $\bar{I}$ to obtain $I(\alpha f) = \alpha I(f)$.

(3) If $f \in \mathcal{L}^1$ and $f \geq 0$, then all approximating functions $\bar{f} \in \bar{B}$ are nonnegative, and thus $I(f) = \inf_{\bar{f} \geq f} \bar{I}(\bar{f}) \geq 0$ since $\bar{I}$ is nonnegative.

(4) Given $\{f_i\}_{i=1}^{\infty}$ in $\mathcal{L}^1$ with $f_i \downarrow 0$ and given $\epsilon > 0$, choose $\underline{f_1} \in \underline{B}$ such that

$$\underline{f_1} \leq f_1 \quad \text{and} \quad I(f_1) - \underline{I}(\underline{f_1}) < \epsilon/2.$$

For $i = 2, 3, \ldots$ choose $\underline{f_i} \in \underline{B}$ such that

$$\underline{f_i} \leq f_i - f_{i-1} \quad \text{and} \quad I(f_i - f_{i-1}) - \underline{I}(\underline{f_i}) < \epsilon/2^i.$$

Define $\underline{F_n} = (\sum_{i=1}^n \underline{f_i}) \vee 0$. Then $\underline{F_n} \in \underline{B}$, $\underline{F_n} \leq f_n$, $\underline{F_n} \downarrow 0$, and

$$I(f_n) - \underline{I}(\underline{F_n}) \leq I(f_1) + \sum_{i=2}^n I(f_i - f_{i-1}) - \sum_{i=1}^n \underline{I}(\underline{f_i})$$

$$= I(f_1) - \underline{I}(\underline{f_1}) + \sum_{i=2}^n (I(f_i - f_{i-1}) - \underline{I}(\underline{f_i})) < \epsilon.$$

By Lemma 4.2c we know that $\underline{I}(\underline{F_n}) \downarrow 0$ and it follows from the above inequality that $I(f_n) \downarrow 0$ since $I(f_n) = (I(f_n) - \underline{I}(\underline{F_n})) + \underline{I}(\underline{F_n})$. This completes the proof.

This completes the integral extension procedure and we emphasize that the extension applied to the Riemann integral (cf. Exercise 4.2) gives the *Lebesgue integral*. Thus our procedure can be thought of as defining an abstract Lebesgue integral, often called the *Daniell integral*.

□ **CLASSICAL CONVERGENCE THEOREMS**

We now have the machinery to develop two of the classical theorems of integration theory. The experienced reader will notice that the theorems are not presented in the more general "almost everywhere" terminology, though this could (but will not) easily be recovered after the next section. All functions except those from $\bar{B}$ and $\underline{B}$ are assumed to be real valued and everywhere defined (on the underlying set S).

THEOREM 4.5 **Monotone Convergence Theorem**
Given $\{f_i\}_{i=1}^{\infty}$ in $\mathcal{L}^1$, $f_i \uparrow f$, and $\lim I(f_i) < \infty$, then $f \in \mathcal{L}^1$ and $I(f_i) \uparrow I(f)$. A similar result holds for monotone decreasing limits, where it is then assumed that $\lim I(f_i) > -\infty$.

□ **PROOF** We prove only the results for increasing limits, using arguments similar to those used for property (4) of Theorem 4.4. Given $\epsilon > 0$ choose $\bar{f}_1 \in \bar{B}$ such that

$$\bar{f}_1 \geq f_1 \quad \text{and} \quad \bar{I}(\bar{f}_1) < I(f_1) + \epsilon/2.$$

For $i = 2, 3, \ldots$, choose $\bar{f}_i \in \bar{B}$ with

$$\bar{f}_i \geq f_i - f_{i-1} \quad \text{and} \quad \bar{I}(\bar{f}_i) < I(f_i - f_{i-1}) + \epsilon/2^i.$$

Define $\bar{F}_i = \sum_{j=1}^{i} \bar{f}_j$. Then $\bar{F}_i \in \bar{B}$, $\bar{F}_i \geq f_i$, $\bar{F}_i \uparrow \bar{f} \in \bar{B}$, $\bar{f} \geq f$, and

$$\bar{I}(\bar{f}) = \lim \bar{I}(\bar{F}_i) = \sum_{j=1}^{\infty} \bar{I}(\bar{f}_j) \quad \text{(by Lemmas 4.2c and 4.3a)}$$

$$< I(f_1) + \epsilon/2 + \sum_{j=2}^{\infty} (I(f_j - f_{j-1}) + \epsilon/2^j)$$

$$\leq \lim I(f_i) + \epsilon < \infty.$$

Now choose n large enough so that $\bar{I}(\bar{f}) - I(f_n) < \epsilon$. Since $f_n \in L^1$ we can find $\underline{f} \in \underline{B}$ with $\underline{f} \leq f_n$ such that $I(f_n) - \underline{I}(\underline{f}) < \epsilon$. This yields $\underline{f} \leq f_n \leq f \leq \bar{f}$ and $\bar{I}(\bar{f}) - \underline{I}(\underline{f}) < 2\epsilon$. Hence $f \in \mathcal{L}^1$ and using property (4') for integrals, $I(f) = \lim I(f_n)$.

The well-known and frequently used result for the interchange of integrals and pointwise limits is

THEOREM 4.6 **Lebesgue Dominated Convergence Theorem**
Given $\{f_i\}_{i=1}^{\infty}$ in $\mathcal{L}^1$, $f_i \to f$ pointwise, and $|f_i| \leq g$ $(i = 1, 2, \ldots)$ for some $g \in \mathcal{L}^1$, then $f \in \mathcal{L}^1$ and $I(f_i) \to I(f)$.

EXERCISE 4.4   Prove Theorem 4.6 with the following hints. Define $\{g_i^k\}_{k=1}^{\infty}$ for each i by $g_i^k = f_i \vee f_{i+1} \vee \cdots \vee f_{i+k}$ and argue that there exists $g_i \in \mathcal{L}^1$ such that $g_i^k \uparrow_k g_i$. Then show that $g_i \downarrow f$, $f \in \mathcal{L}^1$, and $I(g_i) \downarrow I(f)$, so $I(f) \geq \lim I(f_i)$. Show finally that $I(f) = \lim I(f_i)$. Where have you used the crucial hypothesis giving the existence of the dominating function g?

Our general terminology should not disguise the fact that, in **R** for instance, the above theorems give conditions under which limits and integral signs can be interchanged:

$$\lim \int f_i = \int \lim f_i.$$

EXERCISE 4.5   Show that monotone convergence cannot be replaced by point-wise convergence in Theorem 4.5 and that the dominating function g is needed in Theorem 4.6.   Hint: Consider a certain sequence $\{f_i\}$ of step functions on **R** such that $f_i \to 0$ and $\int f_i = 1$.

For what follows we perform one more minor extension of our integral. Let $\mathfrak{B}^+ = \{f \in \mathfrak{B} : f \geq 0\}$ and define I on $\mathfrak{B}^+$ by setting $I(f) = \infty$ if f is not summable (recall f summable means $f \in \mathcal{L}^1$). Given $f \in \mathfrak{B}$, we can write $f = f^+ - f^-$ with $f^+, f^- \in \mathfrak{B}^+$ by letting $f^+ = f \vee 0$ and $f^- = -(f \wedge 0)$. We say that $f \in \mathfrak{B}$ is *integrable* if either f^+ or f^- is summable, and we define $I(f) = I(f^+) - I(f^-)$. Thus every $f \in \mathfrak{B}^+$ is integrable; and an integrable function, though it may have an extended real number as the value of its integral, at least has a well-defined value; this safely avoids the undefined nature of $\infty + (-\infty)$. Note that $f \in \mathfrak{B}$ is summable if and only if f is integrable and $|I(f)| < \infty$. Also

$$|I(f)| = |I(f^+) - I(f^-)| \leq I(f^+) + I(f^-) = I(|f|).$$

LEMMA 4.7   a. Given $f \in \mathfrak{B}$ and $|f| \leq g$ for some $g \in \mathcal{L}^1$, then $f \in \mathcal{L}^1$.
   b. Given f and g integrable with $I(f)$ and $I(g)$ not oppositely infinite, then $f + g$ is integrable and $I(f + g) = I(f) + I(g)$.
   c. Given $\{f_i\}$ integrable, $I(f_i) > -\infty$, and $f_i \uparrow f$, then f is integrable and $I(f_i) \uparrow I(f)$.

$\square$ **PROOF** (a) Define

$$M = \{h \in \mathcal{B} : |h| \leq g \text{ for some } g \in \mathcal{L}^1 \Rightarrow h \in \mathcal{L}^1\}.$$

Clearly $M \supseteq \mathcal{L}$, and M is monotone since $h_i \in M, h_i \uparrow h$, $|h| \leq$ some $g \in \mathcal{L}^1 \Rightarrow h_i \in \mathcal{L}^1$ and hence $h \in \mathcal{L}^1$ by either the monotone or dominated convergence theorem. A similar argument holds for $h_i \in M, h_i \downarrow h$. Thus M is monotone, includes $\mathcal{L}$, and must then be all of $\mathcal{B}$, proving (a).

(b) From the hypotheses we may assume without loss of generality that both f^- and g^- are summable (the argument is similar if both f^+ and g^+ are summable). Then

$$(f + g)^- = -((f + g) \wedge 0) \leq -(f \wedge 0)$$
$$+ (-(g \wedge 0)) = f^- + g^-.$$

By (a) we may conclude that $(f + g)^-$ is summable. Since $f + g \in \mathcal{B}$ we have shown that $f + g$ is integrable. If f and g are summable, then $I(f + g) = I(f) + I(g)$ by Theorem 4.4. Otherwise both values are ∞ and the result still holds.

(c) It is readily checked that $f_i^+ \uparrow f^+$ and $f_i^- \downarrow f^-$. Thus f^+ and f^- belong to $\mathcal{B}$ and $I(f_1) > -\infty$ gives $I(f^-) \leq I(f_1^-) < \infty$. Hence by (a), f^- is summable and thus f is integrable. If $I(f_i^+) \uparrow \infty$, then $I(f_i) \uparrow \infty$ and $I(f) = \infty$. Otherwise the monotone convergence theorem yields $I(f_i^+) \uparrow I(f^+)$ and $I(f_i^-) \downarrow I(f^-)$, so that

$$I(f_i) = (I(f_i^+) - I(f_i^-)) \uparrow (I(f^+) - I(f^-)) = I(f).$$

$\square$ **MEASURES ON σ-ALGEBRAS**

We now introduce the notion of a measure and establish the rather intimate link between measures and integrals obtained from our extension procedure.

Given a set S, a family $\mathbf{S}$ of subsets of S is called a σ-*algebra* if:

(a) $\emptyset \in \mathbf{S}$.
(b) $\mathbf{S}$ is closed under complementation (with respect to S).

(c) $\{A_i\}_{i=1}^{\infty}$ in $\mathbf{S} \Rightarrow \bigcup_{i=1}^{\infty} A_i \in \mathbf{S}$.

A (positive) *measure* μ is an $\mathbf{R}^e$-valued function on a σ-algebra

$\mathcal{S}$ of subsets of S such that:

(a) $\mu(\emptyset) = 0$.
(b) $\mu(A) \geq 0$ for all $A \in \mathcal{S}$ (note that $\infty > 0$).
(c) μ is *countably additive*, i.e., $\{A_i\}_{i=1}^{\infty}$ in $\mathcal{S}$ and pairwise disjoint $(A_i \cap A_j = \emptyset$ if $i \neq j) \Longrightarrow$

$$\mu\left(\bigcup_{i=1}^{\infty} A_i\right) = \sum_{i=1}^{\infty} \mu(A_i).$$

It should be noted that the countable additivity in (c) implies finite additivity,

$$\mu\left(\bigcup_{i=1}^{n} A_i\right) = \sum_{i=1}^{n} \mu(A_i),$$

by choosing $A_i = \emptyset$ for $i = n+1, n+2, \ldots$ and using (a). The definitions of σ-algebra and measure can be thought of as a most natural generalization of the properties of sets that can be assigned an area (length, volume) and of the function which assigns an area to each such set. As will be seen, these ideas are very closely related to those of a linear lattice of functions and an integral. Measures and σ-algebras are also of obvious importance in probability theory, where countable additivity as opposed to just finite additivity plays a crucial role.

Let $\mathcal{L}$ be a linear lattice of functions on a set S. We assume for the duration of the chapter that the collection $\mathcal{B}$ of Baire functions generated by $\mathcal{L}$ satisfies a restricted version of *Stone's hypothesis*: $\mathcal{B}$ contains the function that is identically 1 on S (and hence contains all constant functions).

Given a subset A of S, the *characteristic function* χ_A of A is defined on S by

$$\chi_A(s) = \begin{cases} 1 & \text{if } s \in A \\ 0 & \text{if } s \notin A. \end{cases}$$

Now assuming that an integral I is defined on $\mathcal{L}$, we may apply the theory of the previous sections to ensure that I has undergone the extension procedure. In addition we have, as developed at the end of the preceding section, the extended integral (still called I) whose domain consists of the integrable functions and includes

$\mathcal{B}^+$, the nonnegative functions in $\mathcal{B}$. Thus we can make the following definitions:

A subset A of S is called *measurable* if $\chi_A \in \mathcal{B}^+$ in which case we define the *measure* $\mu(A)$ of A by

$$\mu(A) = I(\chi_A).$$

Recall by the final extension of the previous section that I (with the possible value ∞) is defined on all of $\mathcal{B}^+$.

EXERCISE 4.6 a. Prove that a countable intersection of sets in a σ-algebra is also in the σ-algebra.

b. Let $\mathcal{S}$ be a σ-algebra and μ a measure on $\mathcal{S}$. Given A, $B \in \mathcal{S}$ with $A \subseteq B$, prove that $B \backslash A \in \mathcal{S}$, $\mu(A) \leq \mu(B)$, and $\mu(B \backslash A) = \mu(B) - \mu(A)$.

c. Letting I denote the extension of the Riemann integral on the space $\mathcal{L}$ of Riemann integrable functions on $[0,1]$, argue that the set A of irrational numbers in $[0,1]$ is measurable and determine $\mu(A)$. Do the same for the set A' of rationals in $[0,1]$. Hint: Use the hint to Exercise 4.2c and a convergence theorem from the previous section.

THEOREM 4.8 Given an integral I on a linear lattice $\mathcal{L}$ of functions on a set S, then the collection $\mathcal{S}$ of measurable subsets of S is a σ-algebra, and μ as defined above is a measure on $\mathcal{S}$.

□ **PROOF** Clearly $\emptyset \in \mathcal{S}$ and $\mu(\emptyset) = 0$ since $0 \in B$ and $\mu(\emptyset) = I(0) = 0$. $\mathcal{S}$ is closed under complementation since $\chi_A \in \mathcal{B}^+ \Longrightarrow \chi_{A'} = 1 - \chi_A \in \mathcal{B}^+$ (using Stone's hypothesis). Nonnegativity of μ follows since I is nonnegative on any nonnegative function and hence on any characteristic function. Given a sequence $\{A_i\}$ of members of $\mathcal{S}$ with $A = \bigcup_{i=1}^{\infty} A_i$ and defining $B_n = \bigcup_{i=1}^{n} A_i$, we have $\bigcup_{n=1}^{\infty} B_n = A$ and $\chi_{B_n} \uparrow \chi_A$. Noting that

$$\chi_{B_n} = \chi_{A_1} \vee \chi_{A_2} \vee \cdots \vee \chi_{A_n} \in \mathcal{B}^+$$

we may use Lemma 4.7c to conclude that $\chi_A \in \mathcal{B}^+$ and thus

$A \in \mathbf{S}$. Finally, if the $\{A_i\}$ are pairwise disjoint,

$$I(\chi_{B_n}) = I\left(\sum_{i=1}^{n} \chi_{A_i}\right) = \sum_{i=1}^{n} I(\chi_{A_i})$$

and by Lemma 4.7c, $I(\chi_{B_n}) \uparrow I(\chi_A)$; so

$$\mu(A) = I(\chi_A) = \sum_{i=1}^{\infty} I(\chi_{A_i}) = \sum_{i=1}^{\infty} \mu(A_i).$$

Thus μ is countably additive and hence a measure on the σ-algebra $\mathbf{S}$.

THEOREM 4.9 Given $f \geq 0$ on S and $a > 0$, let $A(a) = \{s \in S : f(s) > a\}$. Then $f \in \mathbf{\mathcal{B}}^+ \Longleftrightarrow A(a)$ is measurable for every $a > 0$.

□ **PROOF** $\Longrightarrow$: If $f \in \mathbf{\mathcal{B}}^+$, then for every $i = 1, 2, \ldots,$

$$f_i = (i(f - f \wedge a)) \wedge 1 \in \mathbf{\mathcal{B}}^+,$$

where a denotes the constant function whose value is a. Also $f_i \uparrow \chi_{A(a)}$, so by Lemma 4.7c, $\chi_{A(a)} \in \mathbf{\mathcal{B}}^+$, and $A(a)$ is measurable.

$\Longleftarrow$: If $A(a)$ is measurable for every $a > 0$, then so is $(A(a))' = \{s \in S : f(s) \leq a\}$. Given $\delta > 1$, define

$$A_m^\delta = A(\delta^m) \cap (A(\delta^{m+1}))', \qquad m = 0, \pm 1, \pm 2, \ldots.$$

Letting $\chi_m^\delta = \chi_{A_m^\delta}$, then $\chi_m^\delta \in \mathbf{\mathcal{B}}^+$ since A_m is measurable, and hence (see Figure 4.2)

$$f_\delta = \sum_{m=-\infty}^{\infty} \delta^m \chi_m^\delta \in \mathbf{\mathcal{B}}^+.$$

Now let $\delta \downarrow 1$ through a suitable sequence of values (for instance $\delta_i = 1 + 1/i$) to obtain $f_\delta \uparrow f$ and hence by Lemma 4.7c, $f \in \mathbf{\mathcal{B}}^+$.

Figure 4.2 is valuable not only as an aid in the final argument that $f_\delta \uparrow f$, but also as an indication of a fundamental difference in approach between the Riemann and Lebesgue integrals. Recall that Riemann integrability of a function f can be defined by par-

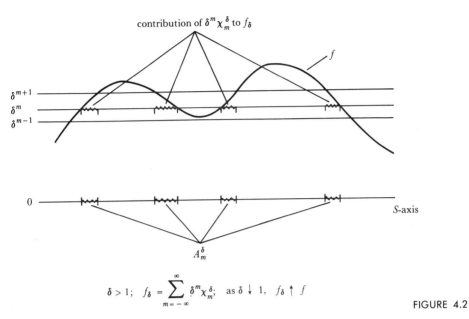

contribution of $\delta^m \chi_m^\delta$ to f_δ

δ^{m+1}

δ^m

δ^{m-1}

f

0

S-axis

A_m^δ

$$\delta > 1; \quad f_\delta = \sum_{m=-\infty}^{\infty} \delta^m \chi_m^\delta; \quad \text{as } \delta \downarrow 1, \quad f_\delta \uparrow f$$

FIGURE 4.2

titioning an interval on the x-axis (domain of f) into finitely many subintervals and by defining two step functions whose heights on each subinterval are respectively the sup and inf of the function values on the subinterval. Partitions are then made finer and finer and, in the event that the naturally defined integrals of the encompassing step functions approach a common limit, we say that f is Riemann integrable and use this common limit as its integral. In the case of the Lebesgue (or more generally, Daniell) integral Figure 4.2 indicates a procedure whereby the y-axis (codomain of f) is partitioned into infinitely many subintervals and generalized step functions (sometimes called *simple* functions) f_δ are obtained. A definition of Lebesgue integrability and a value of the integral are then obtained in a natural fashion.

The powerful arguments of Theorem 4.9 now yield a corollary which states rather surprisingly that the set $\mathscr{B}$ of Baire functions is not only a linear lattice, but also has a multiplicative structure.

COROLLARY (a) $f \in \mathscr{B}^+, b > 0 \Rightarrow f^b \in \mathscr{B}^+$
(b) $f, g \in \mathscr{B} \Rightarrow fg \in \mathscr{B}$

□ **PROOF**   (a) For $f \in \mathcal{B}^+$ and $a, b > 0$, $f^b(s) > a \Leftrightarrow f(s) > a^{1/b}$ and hence $f^b \in \mathcal{B}^+$ by Theorem 4.9.

(b)
$$f, g \in \mathcal{B} \Rightarrow |f \pm g| \in \mathcal{B}^+ \qquad \text{(since } \mathcal{B} \text{ is a linear lattice)}$$
$$\Rightarrow (f + g)^2 \text{ and } (f - g)^2 \in \mathcal{B}^+ \qquad \text{(by } (a))$$
$$\Rightarrow fg = \tfrac{1}{4}[(f + g)^2 - (f - g)^2] \in \mathcal{B}.$$

A function $f \in \mathcal{B}$ is called a *null function* if $I(|f|) = 0$. A *null set* or set of measure 0 is a subset A of S whose characteristic function is a null function—equivalently $\mu(A) = 0$. A function that is a countable (pointwise convergent) sum of null functions is a null function and a countable union of null sets is a null set (why?). Two functions f and g are *equivalent* (written $f \sim g$) if $f - g$ is a null function.

EXERCISE 4.7   Given $f \in \mathcal{B}$, prove that f is a null function $\Leftrightarrow \{s \in S : f(s) \neq 0\}$ is a null set. Hint: Use some of the ideas from the proof of Theorem 4.9.

□ L^p SPACES AND THEIR COMPLETENESS

We now use the space $\mathcal{L}^1$ of summable functions to define general $\mathcal{L}^p$ spaces, $1 \leq p < \infty$. As outlined in Chapter 3, we define
$$\mathcal{L}^p = \{f \in \mathcal{B} : |f|^p \in \mathcal{L}^1\}, \qquad \|f\|_p = (I(|f|^p))^{1/p}.$$

Also we say that $f \in \mathcal{B}$ is *essentially bounded* if f is equivalent to a function $\tilde{f} \in \mathcal{B}$ which is bounded, and we define
$$\mathcal{L}^\infty = \{f \in \mathcal{B} : f \text{ essentially bounded}\}, \quad \|f\|_\infty = \inf_{\tilde{f} \sim f} \left\{ \sup_{s \in S} |\tilde{f}(s)| \right\}.$$

For a general p with $1 \leq p \leq \infty$, we then have $f \in \mathcal{L}^p \Leftrightarrow \|f\|_p < \infty$. While $\|\ \|_p$ is not generally a norm on $\mathcal{L}^p$, we prematurely use the norm notation in anticipation of where we are headed.

EXERCISE 4.8   Prove:

a. $f \in \mathcal{B}$ is a null function $\Leftrightarrow f \in \mathcal{L}^p$ and $\|f\|_p = 0$
($1 \leq p \leq \infty$).

b. Given $f \in \mathcal{B}^+$, then $f \in \mathcal{L}^p \Leftrightarrow f^p \in \mathcal{L}^1$.

c. Given $\{f_i\}$, $f \in \mathcal{L}^1$, $f_i \geq 0$, $f_i \uparrow f$, and $f_i \xrightarrow{\|\ \|_1} f$, then $f_i^{1/p} \xrightarrow{\|\ \|_p} f^{1/p}$. Hint: Given $a, b \geq 0$ and $p \geq 1$ use $a^p + b^p \leq (a + b)^p$ to obtain $a^p \leq (a+ b)^p - b^p$. Now let $a = f^{1/p} - f_i^{1/p}$ and $b = f_i^{1/p}$ and argue that $I(\, |\, f^{1/p} - f_i^{1/p}\, |^{\,p}) \leq I(\, |\, f - f_i\, |\,)$.

We now set about showing that for $1 \leq p \leq \infty$, $\|\ \|_p$ is a seminorm on $\mathcal{L}^p$ which makes $\mathcal{L}^p$ into a complete seminormed linear space.

THEOREM 4.10 **Holder's Inequality**

Given $p, q \geq 1$ satisfying $1/p + 1/q = 1$ and given $f \in \mathcal{L}^p$, $g \in \mathcal{L}^q$, then $fg \in \mathcal{L}^1$ and

$$I(\, |\, fg\, |\,) \leq \|f\|_p \|g\|_q.$$

□ **PROOF** If p or $q = 1$, we interpret that q or $p = \infty$, and the result can be verified easily and directly. Given $x \geq 0$ and $p > 1$ ($p \neq \infty$), an application of the mean value theorem to the function Q defined by $Q(x) = x^{1/p}$ at the points x and 1 gives

$$x^{1/p} - 1 = (x - 1) \cdot 1/p \cdot \bar{x}^{-1+1/p} \quad (\bar{x} \text{ between } 1 \text{ and } x)$$
$$\leq (x - 1) \cdot 1/p \quad (\text{checking } x > 1 \text{ and}$$
$$x < 1 \text{ cases separately}).$$

Setting $x = a/b$ and simplifying, we obtain

$$a^{1/p} b^{1/q} \leq a/p + b/q \quad (\text{also for } b = 0). \tag{1}$$

Given $f \in \mathcal{L}^p$ and $g \in \mathcal{L}^q$, assume $\|f\|_p \neq 0$ and $\|g\|_q \neq 0$ since otherwise (using Exercises 4.7 and 4.8a) $I(\, |\, fg\, |\,) = 0$ and we are done. Now choose for each $s \in S$,

$$a(s) = \frac{|f(s)|^p}{(\|f\|_p)^p} \quad \text{and} \quad b(s) = \frac{|g(s)|^q}{(\|g\|_q)^q}.$$

Then by the corollary to Theorem 4.9 the function $a^{1/p} b^{1/q}$ is in $\mathcal{B}^+$ and, applying I to both sides of (1) which holds for a and b as functions, we obtain

$$\frac{I(\, |\, fg\, |\,)}{\|f\|_p \|g\|_q} \leq \frac{1}{p} + \frac{1}{q} = 1,$$

completing the proof.

COROLLARY Minkowski's Inequality

Given $f, g \in \mathcal{L}^p$ with $p \geq 1$, then $f + g \in \mathcal{L}^p$ and

$$\|f + g\|_p \leq \|f\|_p + \|g\|_p.$$

Thus $\|\ \|_p$ is a seminorm which makes $\mathcal{L}^p$ a seminormed linear space for all p with $1 \leq p \leq \infty$.

□ **PROOF** If $p = \infty$, all follows directly. With $1 \leq p < \infty$,

$$|f + g|^p \leq (2(|f| \vee |g|))^p \leq 2^p(|f|^p + |g|^p).$$

Thus by Lemma 4.7a, $|f + g|^p \in \mathcal{L}^1$ and $f + g \in \mathcal{L}^p$. Also,

$$(\|f + g\|_p)^p \leq I(|f + g|^{p-1}|f|) + I(|f + g|^{p-1}|g|)$$
$$\leq (\|f + g\|_p)^{p-1}\|f\|_p + (\|f + g\|_p)^{p-1}\|g\|_p,$$

where $|f + g| \in \mathcal{L}^p \Rightarrow |f + g|^{p-1} \in \mathcal{L}^{p/p-1} = \mathcal{L}^q$ and Holder's inequality have been used. Dividing by $(\|f + g\|_p)^{p-1}$ (the case where $\|f + g\|_p = 0$ poses no problem), we obtain Minkowski's inequality. The nonnegativity ($\|f\|_p \geq 0$ for all $f \in \mathcal{L}^p$) and homogeneity ($\|\alpha f\|_p = |\alpha|\|f\|_p$) are immediate and thus $\|\ \|_p$ is a seminorm on the real linear space $\mathcal{L}^p$.

The following rather technical lemma is the price we must pay for requiring that our $\mathcal{L}^1$ functions be real valued on all of S instead of playing the "almost everywhere" game by ignoring their behavior or allowing $\pm \infty$ on sets of measure 0. The lemma will be indispensable in proving completeness of $\mathcal{L}^p$.

LEMMA 4.11 Given $1 \leq p < \infty$, $\{g_i\}$ a monotone increasing sequence in $\mathcal{L}^p$, and $\lim \|g_i\|_p < \infty$, then there exist functions $h_i \in \mathcal{L}^p$ with $h_i \sim g_i$ such that $h_i \uparrow h \in \mathcal{L}^p$ and $g_i \xrightarrow{\|\ \|_p} h$ (i.e., $\|h - g_i\|_p \rightarrow 0$).

□ **PROOF** We first consider that case with $\{g_i\}$ in $\mathcal{L}^1$. For each positive integer m and n, define

$$A_{mn} = \{s \in S : g_n(s) > m\}.$$

Then $g_n \in \mathcal{L}^1 \Rightarrow g_n$ integrable $\Rightarrow$ (Theorem 4.9) A_{mn} is measurable for every m and n. Letting $B_m = \bigcup_{n=1}^{\infty} A_{mn}$, the B_m are measurable by Theorem 4.8. We claim $\mu(B_m) \downarrow 0$. Suppose on the contrary that $\mu(B_m) \geq \delta$ for all m and some $\delta > 0$. Then for every m,

$$\lim_i (g_i \wedge m) \in \mathfrak{L}^1$$

by the monotone convergence theorem, and

$$\lim \| g_i \|_1 \geq \| \lim (g_i \wedge m) \|_1$$
$$= I(|\lim (g_i \wedge m)|) \geq I(m\chi_{B_m}) \geq m\delta.$$

This says $\lim \| g_i \|_1 = \infty$, which is a contradiction. We now define $A = \bigcap_{m=1}^{\infty} B_m$ and it follows that $\chi_{B_m} \downarrow \chi_A$, $\chi_{B_m} \in \mathfrak{L}^1$, and certainly $I(\chi_{B_m}) > -\infty$. The monotone convergence theorem gives $\chi_A \in \mathfrak{L}^1$, so A is measurable and

$$\mu(A) = I(\chi_A) = \lim I(\chi_{B_m}) = \lim \mu(B_m) = 0.$$

For each i, define $h_i = g_i \chi_{A'}$ (A' being the complement of A in S). Then $h_i \in \mathfrak{B}$ since $\mathfrak{B}$ is closed under products; $h_i \sim g_i$ since they differ only on a null set; and $\| h_i - g_i \|_1 = 0$. Now $h_i \uparrow h \in \mathfrak{B}$ and by the monotone convergence theorem $h \in \mathfrak{L}^1$, $h_i \xrightarrow{\|\ \|_1} h$ and hence $g_i \xrightarrow{\|\ \|_1} h$. The above argument may now be put to work for general p with $1 \leq p < \infty$ as follows: First consider $\{g_i\}$ in $\mathfrak{L}^p$ with $g_i \geq 0$. Then $g_i^p \in \mathfrak{L}^1$ and by the above we may find $h_i \in \mathfrak{L}^1$, $h_i \geq 0$, such that $h_i \sim g_i^p$, $h_i \uparrow h \in \mathfrak{L}^1$, and $g_i^p \xrightarrow{\|\ \|_1} h$. Then $h_i^{1/p}$ and $h^{1/p}$ are in $\mathfrak{L}^p$ and satisfy the requirements of the theorem (using Exercise 4.8c). For a general sequence $\{g_i\}$ in $\mathfrak{L}^p$ satisfying the hypotheses of the theorem, we use the decomposition $g_i = g_i^+ - g_i^-$ and the fact (Lemma 4.7a) that $g \in \mathfrak{L}^p \iff g^+$ and g^- are in $\mathfrak{L}^p$. Since $\{g_i\}$ is monotone increasing, so is g_i^+ and as above we can obtain the desired $h_i^+ \sim g_i^+$ and h^+ in $\mathfrak{L}^p$. Also g_i^- will be monotone decreasing and the monotone convergence theorem (applied to $(g_i^-)^p \in \mathfrak{L}^1$) will give $h^- \in \mathfrak{L}^p$ as the limit of g_i^-. It then follows that $h_i = (h_i^+ - g_i^-) \sim g_i$ and $h = h^+ - h^-$ satisfy the requirements of the theorem.

THEOREM 4.12 $\mathfrak{L}^p$ is complete for $1 \leq p \leq \infty$.

□   **PROOF**   First suppose $1 \leq p < \infty$. Given $\{f_i\}_{i=1}^{\infty}$ Cauchy in $\mathfrak{L}^p$ we may assume that $\| f_{i+1} - f_i \|_p < 2^{-i}$. This is no loss of generality since we can obtain a subsequence with this property and convergence of this subsequence will imply (Exercise 3.2) convergence of the original Cauchy sequence. For each positive integer m, apply Lemma 4.11 to the $\mathcal{L}^p$ sequence $\{g_{m,i}\}_{i=1}^{\infty}$ where $g_{m,i} = \sum_{j=m+1}^{m+i} |f_j - f_{j-1}|$. We then obtain $h_{m,i} \in \mathcal{L}^p$, $h_{m,i} \sim g_{m,i}$, $h_{m,i} \uparrow_i h_m \in \mathcal{L}^p$, and

$$\|h_m\|_p = \lim_i \|g_{m,i}\|_p \leq \sum_{i=m+1}^{\infty} \|f_i - f_{i-1}\|_p \leq \sum_{i=m}^{\infty} 2^{-i} = 2^{-m+1}.$$

The point of this subterfuge is that we may now think of h_m as $\sum_{j=m+1}^{\infty} |f_j - f_{j-1}|$, though this sum may fail to converge on a set of measure 0. Now define $g_m = f_m - h_m$. Then except on a set of measure 0,

$$g_{m+1} - g_m = f_{m+1} - f_m + |f_{m+1} - f_m| \geq 0.$$

Thus $\{g_m\}$ is a monotone increasing sequence in $\mathcal{L}^p$ and

$$\lim_m \|g_m\|_p \leq \sup_m \|f_m\|_p$$

since Cauchy sequences are bounded. Lemma 4.11 again applies, yielding $f \in \mathcal{L}^p$ such that $\|g_m - f\|_p \to 0$. We then have

$$\|f - f_m\|_p = \lim \|g_m - f_m\|_p = \|h_m\|_p \to 0 \qquad \text{as} \quad m \to \infty,$$

and we have thus found an $\mathcal{L}^p$ limit for the Cauchy sequence $\{f_i\}$. The $\mathcal{L}^\infty$ case is more direct; for if $\{f_i\}$ is Cauchy in $\mathcal{L}^\infty$, we may assume $|f_i(s)| \leq \|f_i\|_\infty$ for all $s \in S$ by replacing f_i by an equivalent function for which this is true. Then $\{f_i(s)\}$ is a Cauchy sequence in $\mathbf{R}$ for each $s \in S$ and we may thus obtain a function f on S. Then f is in $\mathcal{B}$ and hence in $\mathcal{L}$ since $g_i \uparrow f$, where $g_i = f_i \wedge f_{i+1} \wedge \cdots$ and $g_i \in \mathcal{B}$ (why?). It then follows readily that $\|f - f_i\|_\infty \to 0$. This completes the proof.

We are now ready to obtain the Banach spaces L^p as outlined in Chapter 3. For a fixed p with $1 \leq p \leq \infty$, define

$$M = \{f \in \mathcal{L}^p : \|f\|_p = 0\}.$$

Then M is clearly a closed subspace of $\mathcal{L}^p$ and hence by Theorem 3.1, $L^p = \mathcal{L}^p/M$ is a Banach space. A member of L^p should properly be thought of as an equivalence class of functions (indeed a class of equivalent functions), but we conform to standard malpractice by referring to these equivalence classes as functions. Also, we use the same symbol $\|\ \|_p$ for the norm on L^p.

□ THE CONJUGATE SPACE OF AN L^p SPACE

We complete this chapter by considering two integration theory results that will enable us to prove the facts asserted in Chapter 3 about conjugate spaces of L^p spaces. As usual we start with an integral I on a linear lattice $\mathfrak{L}$ of functions on a set S. We employ the notation $L^p(I)$ for the L^p space generated by the extension procedure to emphasize the role played by the integral I. We require for what follows that the initial collection $\mathfrak{L}$ consist only of bounded functions on S. We also impose (in addition to Stone's hypothesis) the condition that I be a *bounded* linear functional on $\mathfrak{L}$ in the sup norm sense that there exist a constant C such that $I(f) \leq C \cdot \sup_{s \in S} |f(s)|$ for all $f \in \mathfrak{L}$. Since I is nonnegative ($f \geq g \Rightarrow I(f) \geq I(g)$), this condition is equivalent to $I(\chi_S) < \infty$ or $\mu(S) < \infty$. This is not a minor imposition since, for instance, the Riemann (or Lebesgue) integral on **R** does not satisfy this condition. However, many of the more general results can be recaptured (see Remarks at the end of the chapter) and we content ourselves with this simplifying restriction.

THEOREM 4.13 Let F be a bounded linear functional on $\mathfrak{L}$. Then F can be written as the difference of two nonnegative bounded linear functionals on $\mathfrak{L}$.

□ **PROOF** Given $f \in \mathfrak{L}$ with $f \geq 0$, define

$$F^+(f) = \sup_{0 \leq g \leq f} \{F(g)\},$$

where we always assume $g \in \mathfrak{L}$. Then F^+ is finitely defined since F is bounded, and it is immediate that F^+ is nonnegative and $F^+(\alpha f) = \alpha F^+(f)$ for all $\alpha \geq 0$. Also

$$F^+(f_1 + f_2) \geq \sup_{\substack{0 \leq g_1 \leq f_1 \\ 0 \leq g_2 \leq f_2}} \{F(g_1 + g_2)\}$$

$$= \sup_{0 \leq g_1 \leq f_1} \{F(g_1)\} + \sup_{0 \leq g_2 \leq f_2} \{F(g_2)\}$$

$$= F^+(f_1) + F^+(f_2).$$

Conversely, if $f_1, f_2 \geq 0$ and $0 \leq g \leq f_1 + f_2$, then $0 \leq f_1 \wedge g \leq f_1$ and $0 \leq g - (f_1 \wedge g) \leq f_2$.

Thus

$$F^+(f_1 + f_2) = \sup_g \{F(g)\} \leq \sup_g \{F(f_1 \wedge g)\}$$
$$+ \sup_g \{F(g - (f_1 \wedge g))\}$$
$$\leq F^+(f_1) + F^+(f_2).$$

Therefore F^+ is additive on nonnegative functions in $\mathcal{L}$ and can be extended to a nonnegative linear functional on $\mathcal{L}$ by $F^+(f) = F^+(f^+) - F^+(f^-)$. Note that F^+ is bounded on $\mathcal{L}$ because

$$|F^+(f)| \leq F^+(|f|) \leq C \cdot \sup_{s \in S} |f(s)|,$$

where the boundedness of F has been used to obtain C. Finally, defining $F^-(f) = F^+(f) - F(f)$, then F^- is nonnegative on $\mathcal{L}$ since $f \geq 0 \Rightarrow F^+(f) \geq F(f) \Rightarrow F^-(f) \geq 0$. Also F^- is clearly a bounded linear functional on $\mathcal{L}$; and since $F = F^+ - F^-$, the proof is complete.

Before stating and proving the Radon–Nikodym theorem we need a lemma which will be proved in a more general context early in the next chapter. Applicability of the lemma depends upon the fact that $L^2(I)$ is a real Hilbert space under the inner product $\langle f, g \rangle = I(fg)$, which is easily checked (completeness was established in the previous section). We use the lemma, deferring its proof. We also take the liberty of continuing our development in the L^p (rather than $\mathcal{L}^p$) setting, treating equivalence classes of functions as individual functions.

LEMMA 4.14 The real Banach (Hilbert) space $L^2(I)$ has the property that for every $\mathcal{J} \in (L^2(I))^*$ there exists a unique $g \in L^2(I)$ such that $\mathcal{J}(f) = I(fg)$ for all $f \in L^2(I)$.

Let I and $\mathcal{J}$ be integrals on the same linear lattice $\mathcal{L}$. (Recall that an integral is a nonnegative linear functional that preserves monotone limits.) We say that $\mathcal{J}$ is *absolutely continuous* with respect to I if

$$\mu_I(A) = 0 \Rightarrow \mu_{\mathcal{J}}(A) = 0$$

where μ_I and $\mu_{\mathcal{J}}$ denote the measures generated by I and $\mathcal{J}$.

THEOREM 4.15   **Radon–Nikodym Theorem**

If the bounded integral $\mathcal{J}$ is absolutely continuous with respect to the bounded integral I, then there exists a unique $f_0 \in L^1(I)$ such that for all $f \in L^1(\mathcal{J})$, $ff_0 \in L^1(I)$ and $\mathcal{J}(f) = I(ff_0)$.

□   **PROOF**   Consider the bounded integral $K = I + \mathcal{J}$ and the space $L^2(K)$. By Holder's inequality,

$$f \in L^2(K) \Longrightarrow f = f \cdot \chi_S \in L^1(K)$$

and

$$|\mathcal{J}(f)| \leq \mathcal{J}(|f|) \leq K(|f|) \leq \|f\|_2 \|\chi_S\|_2$$

where $\| \ \|_2$ denotes the norm in $L^2(K)$ and $\|\chi_S\|_2 < \infty$ since I and $\mathcal{J}$ are bounded. Thus $\mathcal{J}$ is a bounded linear functional on $L^2(K)$ and by Lemma 4.14 stated above there exists a unique $g \in L^2(K)$ such that $\mathcal{J}(f) = K(fg)$ for all $f \in L^2(K)$. We claim g can be regarded as nonnegative (more properly, all members of the equivalence class determined by g are nonnegative except on sets of μ_K measure 0). Indeed suppose $g < 0$ on a set A where $\mu_K(A) > 0$. Then choosing $f = \chi_A$ we would obtain

$$\mathcal{J}(f) = K(fg) = -K(|\chi_A g|) < 0$$

(the strict inequality follows from Exercise 4.7), contradicting the nonnegativity of $\mathcal{J}$. The expansion

$$\mathcal{J}(f) = K(fg) = I(fg) + \mathcal{J}(fg)$$
$$= I(fg) + I(fg^2) + \mathcal{J}(fg^2)$$
$$= \cdots$$
$$= I\left(f\left(\sum_{i=1}^{n} g^i\right)\right) + \mathcal{J}(fg^n)$$

for any $f \in L^2(K)$ provides two conclusions. First, the set where $g \geq 1$ has μ_I measure zero since otherwise the term $I(f(\sum_{i=1}^n g^i))$ could be made to blow up, contradicting boundedness of $\mathcal{J}$. Since $\mathcal{J}$ is absolutely continuous with respect to I, the set where $g \geq 1$ also has $\mu_{\mathcal{J}}$ measure zero and hence $f \geq 0 \Longrightarrow fg^n \downarrow 0$. It follows from the convergence property of integrals that $\mathcal{J}(fg^n) \downarrow 0$. The second conclusion from the above expansion is that if we define $f_0 = \sum_{i=1}^{\infty} g^i$, then, since $f(\sum_{i=1}^n g^i) \uparrow ff_0$, $ff_0 \in L^1(I)$ and $\mathcal{J}(f) = I(ff_0)$. The function f_0 is unique since $g \in L^2(K)$ is unique in

Lemma 4.14 and $g = f_0/(1 + f_0)$ (run the proof backward). Finally, since $\mathcal{J}(f) = I(ff_0)$ for all $f \in L^2(K)$, this equality holds for all $f \in \mathcal{L}$ and hence for all $f \in L^1(\mathcal{J})$ by the nature of our extension procedure.

THEOREM 4.16   Let I be a bounded integral and let $1/p + 1/q = 1$. Then $(L^p(I))^* \cong L^q(I)$ for all $1 \leq p < \infty$ ($p = 1 \Rightarrow q = \infty$).

□   **PROOF**   Holder's inequality shows that every $f \in L^q(I)$ can be regarded as a member F_f of $(L^p(I))^*$ by defining $F_f(g) = I(fg)$, $g \in L^p(I)$. We now show that every $F \in (L^p(I))^*$ has the form F_f for a unique $f \in L^q(I)$. Since F is bounded on $L^p(I)$, $|F(f)| \leq \|F\| \, \|f\|_p$. Since

$$\sup_{s \in S} |f(s)| \leq 1 \implies \|f\|_p \leq (I(\chi_S))^{1/p}$$

$$\implies |F(f)| \leq \|F\|(I(\chi_S))^{1/p},$$

F can be restricted to a bounded linear functional on $\mathcal{L}$ (recall that all functions in $\mathcal{L}$ are assumed to be bounded). Theorem 4.13 then applies, so on $\mathcal{L}$ we have $F = F^+ - F^-$ where F^+ and F^- are bounded nonnegative linear functionals. Given $\{f_i\}_{i=1}^\infty$ and f in $\mathcal{L}$ with $f_i \uparrow f$, it follows from our assumption about the boundedness of I on $\mathcal{L}$ that $\{f_i\}$ and f are in L^p and $f_i \xrightarrow{\|\ \|_p} f$. Since F is continuous on L^p, $F(f_i) \to F(f)$. Hence $F^+(f_i) \uparrow F^+(f)$ and $F^-(f_i) \uparrow F^-(f)$, so F^+ and F^- are bounded integrals on $\mathcal{L}$. Since

$$\mu_I(A) = 0 \implies \|\chi_A\|_p = 0 \implies \chi_A \sim 0$$

$$\implies F(\chi_A) = 0 \implies F^+(\chi_A) = F^-(\chi_A) = 0,$$

it follows that F^+ and F^- are absolutely continuous with respect to I. Applying the Radon–Nikodym theorem to both F^+ and F^-, we obtain f_0^+ and $f_0^- \in L^1(I)$ satisfying the usual conditions. Letting $f_0 = f_0^+ - f_0^-$, we obtain $f_0 \in L^1(I)$ such that $F(g) = I(gf_0)$ for all $g \in L^1(F^+) \cap L^1(F^-)$ and hence for all $g \in L^p(I)$ (since $g \in L^p(I) \Rightarrow F(|g|) < \infty \Rightarrow F^+(|g|)$ and $F^-(|g|) < \infty$). To show that $f_0 \in L^q(I)$, first consider the case where $1 < p < \infty$. Let h be bounded, $h \in L^1(I)$, and $0 \leq h \leq |f_0|$. Then, letting sgn denote the signum function,

$$I(h^q) \leq I(h^{q-1} \cdot \text{sgn}(f_0) f_0)$$
$$= F(h^{q-1} \cdot \text{sgn}(f_0)) \leq \|F\| \|h^{q-1}\|_p$$
$$= \|F\| (I(h^q))^{1/p}.$$

Hence $I(h^q)^{1-1/p} \leq \|F\|$, which says $\|h\|_q \leq \|F\|$. Now choosing a sequence $\{h_i\}$ of such functions with $h_i \uparrow |f_0|$, we obtain $f_0 \in L^q(I)$ and $\|f_0\|_q \leq \|F\|$. When $p = 1$, we establish the above result by contradiction. Suppose $\|f_0\|_\infty \leq \|F\| + \epsilon$ for some $\epsilon > 0$, and take $g = \chi_A$ where

$$A = \{s \in S : |f_0(s)| \geq \|F\| + \epsilon/2\}.$$

Then

$$(\|F\| + \epsilon/2)\mu_I(A) \leq I(|gf_0|)$$
$$= F(g \cdot \text{sgn}(f_0)) \leq \|F\| \|g\|_1 = \|F\|\mu_I(A).$$

This is clearly a contradiction unless $\mu_I(A) = 0$; this, along with the fact that $\epsilon > 0$ was arbitrary, shows $\|f_0\|_\infty \leq \|F\|$ when $p = 1$. Finally, for all p with $1 \leq p < \infty$,

$$\|F\| = \sup_{\|g\|_p \leq 1} |F(g)| = \sup_{\|g\|_p \leq 1} \{I(gf_0)\} \leq \|f_0\|_q$$

by Holder's inequality, so $\|F\| = \|f_0\|_q$. Since it is the case (see Exercise 4.9 following) that $f \neq 0 \Rightarrow F_f \neq 0$, our f_0 (or F_{f_0}) corresponding to F must be unique. This shows that the natural correspondence we have established between $(L^p(I))^*$ and $L^q(I)$ is an isometric isomorphism, completing the proof.

EXERCISE 4.9 Establish the claims of the next to last sentence in the proof of Theorem 4.16. Remember that for $f \in L^q(I)$, $f \neq 0$ means f is not equivalent to the zero function.

□ REMARKS

Integration theory is a vast subject and we have considered only one approach to one aspect of the theory. While our approach has the benefits of directness, rapidity, and adaptability to L^p spaces, there are other more leisurely and transparent approaches. (For example, see Rudin's book [12].) It must also be kept in mind that our approach is highly nonconstructive, serving only to extend integrals and not to create them. Thus we have made little progress toward the famous theorem of Haar that every locally compact (topological) group G admits an essentially unique translation-invariant integral on the space of real-valued continuous functions on G which are zero outside of a compact subset of G [13, Chapter VI].

The decision to begin with integrals rather than measures is a natural one from the standpoint of functional analysis; and while the two ideas are in many contexts interchangeable, it is often convenient to use measures rather than integrals as the focal point. Thus the Radon–Nikodym theorem has an equivalent formulation in terms of measures.

The use of measure theory in functional analysis is valuable and unavoidable in many other contexts besides the L^p spaces. As one example, let S be a locally compact Hausdorff space and consider the Banach space $\mathfrak{C}(S)$. The important Riesz representation theorem states that $(\mathfrak{C}(S))^*$ is identifiable with a linear space consisting of measures on S—another statement of the interchangeability of integrals (more properly in this case linear functionals) and measures.

Much of what has been done in this chapter can be extended to more general situations. First note that we have dealt only with the real L^p spaces. Virtually all results obtained for the real case can be extended to the complex case with a modicum of effort [13, p. 46], and we will use the complex results in Chapter 5. Secondly, the conjugate space results of Theorem 4.16 can be extended from our case of a bounded integral (equivalently, a finite measure space) to a general integral when $p > 1$. Some extension is also possible when $p = 1$—thus with the Lebesgue integral, $(L^1(R))^* = L^\infty(R)$. Thirdly, we note that Theorem 4.16 (with extensions) establishes the reflexivity of $L^p(I)$, $1 < p < \infty$; and that generally $(L^\infty(I))^* \supseteq L^1(I)$ with equality holding if and only if $L^\infty(I)$ is finite dimensional (i.e., S is a finite set or the initial linear lattice $\mathfrak{L}$ is finite dimensional).

The sequence spaces l^p mentioned in Chapter 3 can be developed without reference to integration theory, but it is pleasant to observe that their basic properties (completeness, etc.) are also a very special case of our general development if we choose the appropriate $\mathscr{L}$ and I to start with. This idea is developed in Problem 6.

Noting that $L^2(I)$ is not only reflexive but also self-conjugate and an important example (in a sense the "only" example) of a Hilbert space, we now specialize once more to study this important class of spaces.

□   **PROBLEMS**

1. Given $\{f_i\}$ in L^1 such that $\sum_{i=1}^{\infty} |f_i| \in L^1$, prove that $\sum_{i=1}^{\infty} f_i \in L^1$ and

$$I\left(\sum_{i=1}^{\infty} f_i\right) = \sum_{i=1}^{\infty} I(f_i).$$

2. Show that Theorem 4.5 may fail if the hypothesis that $\lim I(f_i) < \infty$ is removed. Hint: Consider a monotone increasing sequence of step functions on $\mathbf{R}$ all of which are in L^1.

3. Let $\mathbf{S}$ be the σ-algebra consisting of all subsets of the positive integers. Define functions μ_{atom}, μ_{count}, and μ_{sup} on $\mathbf{S}$ by

$$\mu_{\text{atom}}(S) = \begin{cases} 1 & \text{if} \quad 37 \in S \\ 0 & \text{otherwise} \end{cases}$$

$$\mu_{\text{count}}(S) = \begin{cases} \infty & \text{if} \quad S \text{ is infinite} \\ \# \text{ of elements in } S & \text{otherwise} \end{cases}$$

$$\mu_{\text{sup}}(S) = \begin{cases} 0 & \text{if } S = \emptyset \\ \sup_{s \in S} \{s\} & \text{otherwise} \end{cases}$$

Prove that exactly two of the above are measures on $\mathbf{S}$.

4. We have seen how a measure μ on a σ-algebra $\mathbf{S}$ can be obtained from an integral I on a linear lattice $\mathscr{L}$ by performing the extension procedure and defining $\mu(A) = I(\chi_A)$. Conversely, given a measure μ on a σ-algebra $\mathbf{S}$ of subsets of S, the *simple functions* on S are defined by

$$\{f: S \rightarrow \mathbf{R} : f = \sum_{i=1}^{n} a_i \chi_{A_i}, A_i \in \mathbf{S} \text{ and pairwise disjoint}\}.$$

Prove that the simple functions are a linear lattice on S and suggest a definition for an integral I on this lattice (a proof that I is an integral involves certain details that one might wish to skip at this point).

5. Given the L^p spaces obtained by starting with an integral on a linear lattice of functions on a set S:

   a. Prove $\mu(S) < \infty$ and $1 \leq p < p' \leq \infty \Rightarrow L^{p'} \subseteq L^p$.
   b. Show that the result of (a) need not be true if $\mu(S) = \infty$.
   c. By using the Lebesgue (or Riemann) integral on a suitable subset of $\mathbf{R}$, show that there exists $f \in L^1$ for which $f \notin L^2$.
   d. Generalize (c) to showing that $1 \leq p < p' < \infty \Rightarrow$ there exists $f \in L^p$ for which $f \notin L^{p'}$.

6. Recall the l^p spaces defined early in Chapter 3.

   a. By defining an appropriate integral I on an appropriate collection $\mathcal{L}$ of functions on an appropriate set S, obtain the l^p spaces by invoking the extension procedure. Make your choices of $\mathcal{L}$ and I as simple as possible and show directly that I is an integral on $\mathcal{L}$. Conclude that the l^p spaces are normed, complete, and for $1 < p < \infty$ describe $(l^p)^*$. Hints: Sequences can be viewed as functions on the set of positive integers; and if $\{x_i\}_{i=1}^\infty$ is a sequence whose components beyond x_n are 0, define $I(\{x_i\}) = \sum_{i=1}^n x_i$.
   b. With respect to your simple choice of $\mathcal{L}$ what do $\mathcal{B}$, $\overline{B}$, and $\underline{B}$ look like? What is the measure arising from the extension of I on $\mathcal{L}$ to I on L^1? What is the σ-algebra $\mathcal{S}$?

Hilbert Space

5

□ DEFINITION AND BASIC PROPERTIES

Hilbert space can be viewed as arising from a natural general-ization of properties of finite-dimensional Euclidean spaces. While Hilbert's initial investigations leading to the class of spaces named for him were not exactly based on this fact (but rather on a study of quadratic forms), it is highly pleasing that the revolu-tionary and far-reaching ideas of Hilbert specialize to such a familiar setting. The crowning glory of Hilbert's study is that Hilbert space is also a natural setting for one important formula-tion of quantum mechanics. While Hilbert essentially studied sequence spaces (l^2) and physicists tend to consider spaces of functions (L^2), the most elegant and mathematically economical formulation regards Hilbert space as a linear space with certain very special properties.

A *Hilbert space* H is a complete, complex, inner product space. Thus H is a complex linear space that has associated with it a conjugate bilinear functional $\langle , \rangle : H \times H \rightarrow \mathbf{C}$ satisfying for all $x, y, z \in H$ and $\alpha, \beta, \in \mathbf{C}$:

(a) $\langle x, y \rangle = \langle y, x \rangle^*$ (* is complex conjugation)
(b) $\langle \alpha x + \beta y, z \rangle = \alpha \langle x, z \rangle + \beta \langle y, z \rangle$
(c) $\langle x, x \rangle \geq 0$, and $\langle x, x \rangle = 0 \Rightarrow x = 0$;

and H is a Banach space under the norm $\| x \| = \langle x, x \rangle^{1/2}$. Indeed $\| \ \|$ is a norm by:

THEOREM 5.1 For all $x, y, \in H$,

(a) $| \langle x, y \rangle | \leq \| x \| \ \| y \|$ (Schwarz inequality).
(b) $\| x + y \| \leq \| x \| + \| y \|$ and hence $\| \ \|$ is a norm on H.

□ **PROOF** (a) If $\| y \| = 0$, then

$$\langle x, y \rangle = \langle x, 0 \rangle = \langle 0, x \rangle^* = \langle 0 \cdot x, x \rangle^* = 0 \langle x, x \rangle^* = 0,$$

and the inequality is immediate. Assuming $\| y \| \neq 0$, let $\alpha = \langle x, y \rangle / \| y \|^2$ in the following inequality:

$$0 \leq \| x - \alpha y \|^2 = \langle x - \alpha y, x - \alpha y \rangle$$
$$= \| x \|^2 - \alpha^* \langle x, y \rangle - \alpha \langle x, y \rangle^* + | \alpha |^2 \| y \|^2.$$

The desired result falls out by some pleasant simplification and cancellation in the final expression (recall $\alpha \cdot \alpha^* = |\alpha|^2$).

(b)

$$\|x + y\|^2 = \langle x + y, x + y \rangle = \|x\|^2 + 2 \cdot \mathrm{Re} \langle x, y \rangle + \|y\|^2$$
$$\leq \|x\|^2 + 2\|x\| \|y\| + \|y\|^2$$
$$= (\|x\| + \|y\|)^2$$

where Schwarz's inequality has been used in the inequality step. The other properties making $\|\ \|$ a norm follow directly.

We will refer to a *real* linear space satisfying all other Hilbert space requirements as a real Hilbert space.

EXERCISE 5.1 Let H be any Hilbert space (for purposes of Euclidean geometry, H can be thought of as the *real* Hilbert space $\mathbf{R}^2$ or $\mathbf{R}^3$).

a. Prove the "Pythagorean theorem" in H:

$$\langle x, y \rangle = 0 \Longrightarrow \|x\|^2 + \|y\|^2 = \|x + y\|^2.$$

b. Given $x, y \in H$ define the "angle between x and y" by

$$\theta_{x,y} = \begin{cases} 0 & \text{if } x \text{ or } y = 0 \\ \arccos\left(\mathrm{Re} \langle x, y \rangle / (\|x\| \|y\|)\right) & \text{otherwise.} \end{cases}$$

Argue that $\theta_{x,y}$ is well defined and prove the "law of cosines":

$$\|x\|^2 + \|y\|^2 = \|x + y\|^2 - 2\|x\| \|y\| \cos(\theta_{x,y}).$$

The norm arising from an inner product satisfies the *parallelogram law*

$$\|x + y\|^2 + \|x - y\|^2 = 2\|x\|^2 + 2\|y\|^2$$

as is easily seen by expansion of $\langle x \pm y, x \pm y \rangle$. Conversely, if a norm satisfies the parallelogram law, then there exists a unique inner product from which the norm arises. In fact the inner product determined by such a norm is given by

$$\langle x, y \rangle = \sum_{n=1}^{4} i^n \|x + i^n y\| \qquad (i^2 = -1),$$

though we omit the somewhat burdensome details of this computation. The pleasant result of the above is that Hilbert spaces are precisely those complex Banach spaces whose norms satisfy the parallelogram law.

As our example of Hilbert space consider any complex space $L^2(I)$ of square summable functions on a set S as obtained in Chapter 4. (Recall that we actually only treated real spaces in Chapter 4, accepting the rather natural extension to complex-valued functions.) The reader is again urged to keep the Lebesgue integral and Lebesgue measure on a subset S of $\mathbf{R}$ in mind. If we define $\langle f,g \rangle = I(fg^*)$, Holder's inequality (Theorem 4.10) with $p = q = 2$ shows that for $f,g \in L^2(I)$, fg^* is in $L^1(I)$ and $\langle\,,\,\rangle$ is easily seen to be an inner product on $L^2(I)$. Since $L^2(I)$ is complete, it is a Hilbert space.

If the underlying set S is a countably infinite set (say the positive integers) endowed with the counting measure ($\mu(A) =$ cardinality of A), we obtain (cf. Problem 4.6) the Hilbert space l^2 of *square summable sequences,*

$$\langle x,y \rangle = \sum_{i=1}^{\infty} x_i y_i^* \qquad (x = \{x_i\}_{i=1}^{\infty}, \quad y = \{y_i\}_{i=1}^{\infty}).$$

If S is a finite set with n members, this procedure results in the finite-dimensional Hilbert spaces $\mathbf{C}^n$ with the Euclidean norm. In each of these special cases the crucial Hilbert space properties (a well-defined inner product, completeness) follow from our general results for $L^2(I)$. Indeed it turns out that $L^2(I)$, for an appropriately chosen I, $\mathcal{L}$, and S, is essentially the "only" example—all Hilbert spaces being obtainable in this way (see Problem 5.1).

□ **ORTHOGONALITY AND ORTHOGONAL COMPLEMENTS**

Two elements x and y in a Hilbert space are called *orthogonal* if $\langle x,y \rangle = 0$. This terminology derives ample motivation from the *real* Hilbert space $\mathbf{R}^2$ where the vectors $x = (x_1,x_2)$ and $y = (y_1,y_2)$ are perpendicular or orthogonal precisely when $\langle x,y \rangle = x_1 y_1 + x_2 y_2 = 0$. The following result also has natural geometric and finite-dimensional antecedents.

THEOREM 5.2 A closed convex subset C of a Hilbert space H contains a unique element of smallest norm, i.e., there exists exactly one $x \in C$ such that $\|x\| = \inf_{y \in C} \|y\|$.

□ **PROOF** Let $\delta = \inf_{y \in C} \|y\|$ and let $\{x_n\}$ be any sequence in C such that $\|x_n\| \to \delta$. Clearly such sequences exist. Using the parallelogram law we may write

$$\|x_m + x_n\|^2 + \|x_m - x_n\|^2 = 2(\|x_m\|^2 + \|x_n\|^2). \tag{1}$$

Since C is convex, $\frac{1}{2}(x_m + x_n) \in C$ and hence $\|x_m + x_n\|^2 = 4\|\frac{1}{2}(x_m + x_n)\|^2 \geq 4\delta^2$. Solving for $\|x_m - x_n\|^2$ in (1) and letting $m, n \to \infty$ we have $\|x_m\|^2 \to \delta^2$, $\|x_n\|^2 \to \delta^2$, and thus $\|x_m - x_n\|^2 \to 0$, showing that $\{x_n\}$ is a Cauchy sequence. Since H is complete and C is closed, there exists $x \in C$ such that $x_n \to x$, and $\|x\| = \delta$ by continuity of the norm. Finally, x is unique since given $y \in C$ with $\|y\| = \delta$, the above argument can be applied to the sequence $x, y, x, y, x, y, \ldots$ to show that it is Cauchy, which can only be the case if $x = y$.

LEMMA 5.3 Let H be a Hilbert space and M a proper closed subspace. Then there exists a (clearly not unique) nonzero $z \in H$ such that $\langle z, m \rangle = 0$ for all $m \in M$.

□ **PROOF** Given any $x \in H$, the set $x + M$ is a closed convex set. Thus by Theorem 5.2 there exists a unique $z \in H$ such that $z \in x + M$ and $\|z\| = \inf_{m \in M} \|x + m\|$. We shall show that $\langle z, m \rangle = 0$ for all $m \in M$ (and if we choose $x \notin M$, then $z \neq 0$). Indeed given any $m \in M$ and any $\alpha \in \mathbf{C}$, we have $z + \alpha m \in x + M$. By our choice of z we then have $\|z + \alpha m\|^2 \geq \|z\|^2$ and, expanding,

$$|\alpha|^2 \|m\|^2 + 2 \cdot \mathrm{Re}\,(\alpha^* \langle z, m \rangle) \geq 0 \qquad \text{for all} \quad \alpha \in C.$$

Choose $\theta \in [0, 2\pi)$ with $e^{-i\theta} \langle z, m \rangle = |\langle z, m \rangle|$ and let $\alpha = te^{i\theta}$, $t \in \mathbf{R}$. The inequality obtained by substituting for α is then $t^2 \|m\|^2 + 2t |\langle z, m \rangle| \geq 0$ for all $t \in \mathbf{R}$. By choosing t negative and letting t approach zero we obtain $\langle z, m \rangle = 0$ since otherwise the negative term would eventually dominate the positive term and contradict the inequality. Since $m \in M$ was arbitrary, we thus have $\langle z, m \rangle = 0$ for all $m \in M$.

We define for any subset S of H the *orthogonal complement* $S^\perp$ of S by

$$S^\perp = \{x \in H : \langle x, y \rangle = 0 \quad \text{for all} \quad y \in S\}.$$

Note that this definition differs from our locally convex space definition of $\perp$ in that $S^\perp$ is a subset of H rather than of H^*. It will soon be seen that this difference is reconciled through a natural identification of H and H^*.

EXERCISE 5.2 a. Given $y \in H$, define $L_y : H \to \mathbf{C}$ by $L_y(x) = \langle x, y \rangle$. Prove that $L_y \in H^*$ and $\|L_y\| = \|y\|$.

b. Prove that for any subset S of H, $S^\perp$ is a closed subspace of H. Hint: Use (a).

c. Prove that $\langle x, y \rangle = \langle x, z \rangle$ for all $x \in H \Longrightarrow y = z$. Hint: Let $x = y - z$.

We recall that given a linear space Z and subspaces X and Y, Z is defined to be the *direct sum* of X and Y, written $Z = X \oplus Y$, if every $z \in Z$ can be expressed uniquely in the form $z = x + y$, $x \in X$ and $y \in Y$. Equivalently, it is easy to see that $Z = X \oplus Y$ if $Z = X + Y$ and $X \cap Y = \{0\}$. We now prove a theorem about decomposing Hilbert space into a direct sum of mutually orthogonal closed subspaces.

THEOREM 5.4 If M is a closed subspace of a Hilbert space H, then

$$H = M \oplus M^\perp.$$

□ **PROOF** Given $x \in H$, apply the procedure in the proof of Lemma 5.3 to obtain $z \in H$ such that $z \in x + M$ and $\langle z, m \rangle = 0$ for all $m \in M$. Then $z \in M^\perp$ and $z = x - m$ for some $m \in M$. Hence $x = m + z$, $m \in M$, and $z \in M^\perp$. Noting that $M \cap M^\perp = \{0\}$ since

$$x \in M \cap M^\perp \Longrightarrow \langle x, x \rangle = 0 \Longrightarrow x = 0,$$

we thus have $H = M \oplus M^\perp$. Observe that $M^\perp$ is closed by Exercise 5.2b.

□ **THE CONJUGATE SPACE H^***

We now consider an important theorem a special case of which was used (without proof) in proving the Radon–Nikodym theorem (Theorem 4.15).

THEOREM 5.5 Given a Hilbert space H and $y \in H$, define $L_y: H \to \mathbf{C}$ by $L_y(x) = \langle x, y \rangle$. Then $L_y \in H^*$ and $\|L_y\| = \|y\|$. Conversely, for every $f \in H^*$ there exists a unique $y \in H$ such that $f = L_y$.

□ **PROOF** The fact that H is isometrically imbedded in H^* via $y \mapsto L_y$ is the content of Exercise 5.2a. Conversely, let $f \in H^*$ be given. If $f = 0$, then $f = L_y$ where $y = 0$. If $f \neq 0$, we may assume without loss of generality that $\|f\| = 1$ since $f/\|f\| = L_y \Rightarrow f = L_{\|f\|y}$. For such an f, let $M = \ker(f)$ and we claim that $M^\perp$ is a one-dimensional subspace of H (cf. Lemma 2.4b). Suppose, on the contrary, that $z_1, z_2 \in M^\perp$ are linearly independent. Then $f(z_1)$ and $f(z_2)$ are linearly independent in $\mathbf{C}$ since

$$\alpha_1 f(z_1) + \alpha_2 f(z_2) = 0 \Rightarrow f(\alpha_1 z_1 + \alpha_2 z_2) = 0$$
$$\Rightarrow \alpha_1 z_1 + \alpha_2 z_2 \in M \cap M^\perp$$
$$\Rightarrow \alpha_1 z_1 + \alpha_2 z_2 = 0$$
$$\Rightarrow \alpha_1 = \alpha_2 = 0.$$

Since $\mathbf{C}$ is a one-dimensional vector space over itself, this is clearly a contradiction. Now define y to be that unique member of $M^\perp$ such that $f(y) = 1$. It follows that $\|y\| = 1$ since otherwise we would not have $\|f\| = 1$ (this requires some checking). We will show that $L_y = f$. Indeed for any $x \in H$ the fact that $H = M \oplus M^\perp$ shows that $x = m + \beta y$, $m \in M$ and $\beta \in \mathbf{C}$. Thus

$$L_y(x) = \langle x, y \rangle = \langle m + \beta y, y \rangle = \langle m, y \rangle + \beta \langle y, y \rangle$$
$$= 0 + \beta = f(m) + \beta f(y) = f(m + \beta y)$$
$$= f(x).$$

Finally, our choice of y is unique, for $L_y = L_z \Rightarrow \langle x, y \rangle = \langle x, z \rangle$ for all $x \in H \Rightarrow y = z$ by Exercise 5.2c.

COROLLARY   Given any Hilbert space H:

    a. $H\ "=" H^*$.
    b. H is reflexive.
    c. The closed unit ball in H is weakly compact.

    □ **PROOF**   (a) We have just exhibited an isometry L from H onto H^* by means of the rule $L(y) = L_y$. Furthermore it is easily seen that $L_{y_1+y_2} = L_{y_1} + L_{y_2}$ so the isometry is additive. Alas it is not, however, homogeneous, but rather

$$L_{\alpha y}(x) = \langle x, \alpha y \rangle = \alpha^* \langle x, y \rangle = \alpha^* L_y(x),$$

so $L_{\alpha y} = \alpha^* L_y$. We nonetheless have a natural conjugate linear isometry from H onto H^*, and in this sense we say $H\ "=" H^*$. Note that the inherited inner product on H^* must be defined by $\langle L_x, L_y \rangle = \langle y, x \rangle$ so that its action on the *second* variable will be conjugate linear.

    (b) By (a) it is clear that $\hat{H} = H^{**}$, and for normed linear spaces this implies reflexivity.

    (c) This follows either from the Banach–Alaoglu theorem and (a) (note that the weak topology on H corresponds to the weak* topology on H^*) or else from (b) and Theorem 3.7.

    □ **ORTHONORMAL BASES
    AND FOURIER ANALYSIS**

    We now develop about Hilbert space some ideas which are singular both for their beauty and for the wealth of applications to science that they provide. We define a subset S of a Hilbert space H to be *orthogonal* if $x, y \in S$ and $x \neq y \implies \langle x, y \rangle = 0$. An *orthonormal* set is an orthogonal set consisting entirely of elements of norm 1.

EXERCISE 5.3   a. Prove that any orthogonal set $\{x_s\}_{s \in I}$ that does not include the 0 vector is linearly independent. Hint: If $\sum_{i=1}^n \alpha_i x_{s_i} = 0$, inner product both sides with $x_{s_j}, j = 1, 2, \ldots, n$.

    b. Prove that if e and f are any two distinct elements of a given orthonormal set, then $\| e - f \| = \sqrt{2}$.

A well-known and constructive result about orthonormal sets is:

THEOREM 5.6   **Gram–Schmidt Orthonormalization**
Given any countable linearly independent subset $\{x_i\}$ of a Hilbert space H, an orthonormal set $\{e_i\}$ can be constructed so that $\mathrm{span}\,(\{e_i\}_{i=1}^n) = \mathrm{span}\,(\{x_i\}_{i=1}^n)$ for all n.

□ **PROOF**   Define $e_1 = x_1/\|x_1\|$ and, proceeding inductively, if $\{e_i\}_{i=1}^n$ are successfully defined, define

$$e_{n+1} = y_{n+1}/\|y_{n+1}\|$$

where $y_{n+1} = x_{n+1} - \sum_{i=1}^n \langle x_{n+1}, e_i \rangle e_i$. Then $\|y_{n+1}\| \neq 0$ since otherwise we would have

$$x_{n+1} \in \mathrm{span}\,(\{e_i\}_{i=1}^n) = \mathrm{span}\,(\{x_i\}_{i=1}^n),$$

contradicting the linear independence of the $\{x_i\}$. It is clear that $\mathrm{span}\,(\{e_i\}_{i=1}^{n+1}) = \mathrm{span}\,(\{x_i\}_{i=1}^{n+1})$ since this is true for $\{e_i\}_{i=1}^n$ and $\{x_i\}_{i=1}^n$. Finally, for $j \le n$,

$$\langle e_{n+1}, e_j \rangle = \left\langle x_{n+1} - \sum_{i=1}^n \langle x_{n+1}, e_i \rangle e_i, e_j \right\rangle / \|y_{n+1}\|$$

$$= \left(\langle x_{n+1}, e_j \rangle - \langle x_{n+1}, e_j \rangle \langle e_j, e_j \rangle \right) / \|y_{n+1}\| = 0,$$

so the set $\{e_i\}$ obtained by this inductive construction is an orthonormal set with the desired property.

LEMMA 5.7   Given a finite orthonormal set $\{e_i\}_{i=1}^n$ and any $x \in H$:

(a) $\sum_{i=1}^n |\langle x, e_i \rangle|^2 \le \|x\|^2$.
(b) $\langle x - \sum_{i=1}^n \langle x, e_i \rangle e_i, e_j \rangle = 0$ for all $j = 1, 2, \ldots, n$.

□ **PROOF**   (a) $0 \le \|x - \sum_{i=1}^n \langle x, e_i \rangle e_i\|^2 = \|x\|^2 - \sum_{i=1}^n |\langle x, e_i \rangle|^2$, where the equality is obtained by expanding in the usual fashion and using orthonormality of $\{e_i\}_{i=1}^n$.
(b) $\langle x - \sum_{i=1}^n \langle x, e_i \rangle e_i, e_j \rangle = \langle x, e_j \rangle - \langle x, e_j \rangle \langle e_j, e_j \rangle = 0$.

COROLLARY   Given an orthonormal set $\{e_\alpha\}_{\alpha \in I}$ (I any index set) and given any $x \in H$, then the set $S = \{e_\alpha : \langle x, e_\alpha \rangle \neq 0\}$ is countable.

□ **PROOF** For each positive integer n, define

$$S_n = \{e_\alpha : |\langle x, e_\alpha \rangle|^2 > \|x\|^2/n\}.$$

By Lemma 5.7a each S_n contains at most $n - 1$ members. Since $S = \bigcup_{n=1}^{\infty} S_n$, S must be countable.

Given an arbitrary orthonormal set $\{e_\alpha\}_{\alpha \in I}$, we would like to extend the results of Lemma 5.7. Using Lemma 5.7 and its corollary, we denote by $\sum_\alpha |\langle x, e_\alpha \rangle|^2$ and $\sum_\alpha \langle x, e_\alpha \rangle e_\alpha$ the series $\sum_{i=1}^{\infty} |\langle x, e_{\alpha_i} \rangle|^2$ and $\sum_{i=1}^{\infty} \langle x, e_{\alpha_i} \rangle e_{\alpha_i}$ respectively, where we restrict ourselves to the countable number of e_{α_i} for which $\langle x, e_{\alpha_i} \rangle \neq 0$. Lemma 5.7a and standard results about the freedom of term rearrangement in an absolutely convergent series show that $\sum_\alpha |\langle x, e_\alpha \rangle|^2$ is well defined. To reach a similar conclusion for $\sum_\alpha \langle x, e_\alpha \rangle e_\alpha$ a completeness argument must be applied to the (Cauchy) sequence of partial sums of any given representation $\sum_{i=1}^{\infty} \langle x, e_{\alpha_i} \rangle e_{\alpha_i}$. We omit the details.

THEOREM 5.8 Given an orthonormal set $\{e_\alpha\}_{\alpha \in I}$ and any $x \in H$:

(a) $\sum_\alpha |\langle x, e_\alpha \rangle|^2 \leq \|x\|^2$ (Bessel's inequality).
(b) $\langle x - \sum_\alpha \langle x, e_\alpha \rangle e_\alpha, e_\beta \rangle = 0$ for all $\beta \in I$.

□ **PROOF** (a) $\sum_\alpha |\langle x, e_\alpha \rangle|^2 = \lim_{n \to \infty} \sum_{i=1}^{n} |\langle x, e_{\alpha_i} \rangle|^2 \leq \|x\|^2$, where the inequality is a direct consequence of Lemma 5.7a.

(b) By using continuity of the inner product in its left-hand variable (which follows from Schwarz's inequality) we obtain

$$\left\langle x - \sum_\alpha \langle x, e_\alpha \rangle e_\alpha, e_\beta \right\rangle = \langle x, e_\beta \rangle - \left\langle \sum_\alpha \langle x, e_\alpha \rangle e_\alpha, e_\beta \right\rangle$$

$$= \langle x, e_\beta \rangle - \left\langle \lim_{n \to \infty} \sum_{i=1}^{n} \langle x, e_{\alpha_i} \rangle e_{\alpha_i}, e_\beta \right\rangle$$

$$= \langle x, e_\beta \rangle - \lim_{n \to \infty} \left\langle \sum_{i=1}^{n} \langle x, e_{\alpha_i} \rangle e_{\alpha_i}, e_\beta \right\rangle$$

$$= \langle x, e_\beta \rangle - \langle x, e_\beta \rangle = 0.$$

The collection E of all orthonormal subsets of H is clearly nonempty and can be partially ordered under inclusion. We define an orthonormal set $\{e_\alpha\}$ to be a *complete* orthonormal set or an *orthonormal basis* for H if $\{e_\alpha\}$ is a maximal element of E. Less formally, this says that an orthonormal set is an orthonormal basis if it is impossible to adjoin an additional element to the set while still preserving its orthonormality.

THEOREM 5.9   Let $\{e_\alpha\}$ be an orthonormal set in H. Then the following are equivalent:

a. $\{e_\alpha\}$ is an orthonormal basis.
b. The closed linear span of $\{e_\alpha\}$ is H.
c. $\langle x, e_\alpha \rangle = 0$ for all $e_\alpha \Rightarrow x = 0$.
d. For all $x \in H$, $x = \sum_\alpha \langle x, e_\alpha \rangle e_\alpha$.
e. For all $x, y \in H$, $\langle x, y \rangle = \sum_\alpha \langle x, e_\alpha \rangle \langle y, e_\alpha \rangle^*$.
f. For all $x \in H$, $\| x \|^2 = \sum_\alpha |\langle x, e_\alpha \rangle|^2$ (Parseval's identity).

EXERCISE 5.4   Prove Theorem 5.9.

As an important special case of the above results, let $H = L^2([0,2\pi))$ and define $\{e_k\}_{k=-\infty}^\infty$ in $L^2([0,2\pi))$ by

$$e_k(x) = (2\pi)^{-1/2} e^{ikx}.$$

Recalling that the function $e^{i\theta} = \cos(\theta) + i\sin(\theta)$ has period 2π, we readily see that $\{e_k\}$ is an orthonormal set:

$$\langle e_j, e_k \rangle = \int_0^{2\pi} e_j e_k^* = \int_0^{2\pi} e_j e_{-k} = \begin{cases} 1 & \text{if } k = j \\ 0 & \text{otherwise.} \end{cases}$$

The completeness of $\{e_k\}$ is a fundamental result in the theory of Fourier series. Given $f \in L^2([0,2\pi))$, the complex numbers $\alpha_k = \langle f, e_k \rangle$ are called the *Fourier coefficients* of f, $\sum_{k=-\infty}^\infty \alpha_k e_k$ is called the *Fourier series* of f, and Theorem 5.9 says that (with convergence and equality interpreted in the L^2 sense) $f = \sum_{k=-\infty}^\infty \alpha_k e_k$. Another important consequence (often called the Riesz–Fischer theorem) of the above is that the mapping which takes $f \in L^2([0,2\pi))$ into its sequence $\{\alpha_k\}_{k=-\infty}^\infty$ of Fourier coefficients is an inner-product-preserving isomorphism between $L^2([0,2\pi))$ and $l^2(\mathbb{Z})$ (the two-way square summable sequences), showing that these two Hilbert spaces are essentially the same. Note that, subject to the fact $\{e_k\}_{k=-\infty}^{\infty}$ is an orthonormal basis, all the above follows from our general development.

We may apply this Fourier analysis to other L^2 spaces, whereupon the natural orthonormal bases are some of the well-known functions of classical analysis. To drop a few names, functions (or polynomials) associated with the nineteenth century mathematicians Chebyshev, Hermite, Laguerre, and Legendre arise in this way. Applications of these ideas abound in differential equations, applied mathematics, physics, and chemistry.

The avenues of extension and generalization of these ideas are vast, giving rise to a major branch of functional analysis generally known as harmonic analysis, whose natural domain is locally compact groups. A standard work in this field is Loomis' book [13].

EXERCISE 5.5 Using the results asserted above about Fourier series, consider $f \in L^2([0,2\pi))$ where $f(x) = x$.

a. Show that

$$\langle f, e_k \rangle = (2\pi)^{-1/2} \int_0^{2\pi} f(x) e^{-ikx} \, dx$$

$$= (2\pi)^{-1/2} \cdot \begin{cases} 2\pi^2, & k = 0 \\ 2\pi i/k, & k = \pm 1, \pm 2, \ldots. \end{cases}$$

b. Using $e^{i\theta} = \cos(\theta) + i \cdot \sin(\theta)$, conclude that x "$=$" $\pi - 2 \sum_{k=1}^{\infty} \sin(kx)/k$ where "$=$" means in the L^2 sense.

c. Make some intelligent guesses about pointwise equality of x and $\pi - 2 \sum_{k=1}^{\infty} \sin(kx)/k$ for $x \in [0,2\pi)$, and then "determine" the value of the series $\sum_{k=0}^{\infty} (-1)^k/(2k+1)$.

Returning now to a general Hilbert space, we may use the Gram–Schmidt orthonormalization to obtain an orthonormal basis provided the space has finite or countably infinite dimension as a vector space (but recall Exercise 3.7b!). In the general case we must resort to our old friend Zorn's lemma.

THEOREM 5.10 Every Hilbert space H has an orthonormal basis, and any two orthonormal bases have the same cardinality.

□ **PROOF** Let E denote the collection of all orthonormal subsets of H. If F is any totally ordered subcollection of E, the set $U = \bigcup_{S \in F} S$ is a member of E and an upper bound for F. An application of Zorn's lemma then establishes the existence of a maximal element for E and hence an orthonormal basis for H. Let $\{e_\alpha\}_{\alpha \in A}$ and $\{f_\beta\}_{\beta \in B}$ be any two orthonormal bases for H. If either A or B is finite, then both have cardinality equal to the linear dimension of H. If A and B are both infinite sets, let S denote the dense set consisting of finite linear combinations from $\{f_\beta\}$ whose scalars have rational real and imaginary parts. It is a standard (but not so easily verified) result that $card(S) = card(B)$, where $card(S)$ denotes the cardinality of S. Given any $e_\alpha, \alpha \in A$, we can obtain a member x_α of S such that $\|e_\alpha - x_\alpha\| \le \frac{1}{2}$ (recall Theorem 5.9b). Since for any distinct $\alpha_1, \alpha_2 \in A$ Exercise 5.3b shows $\|e_1 - e_2\| = \sqrt{2} > 1$ we have just defined an *injective* map ($\alpha \mapsto x_\alpha$) from A into S. Indeed

$$x_{\alpha_1} = x_{\alpha_2} \Rightarrow \|e_{\alpha_1} - e_{\alpha_2}\| \le \|e_{\alpha_1} - x_{\alpha_1}\| + \|x_{\alpha_2} - e_{\alpha_2}\| \le 1$$
$$\Rightarrow \alpha_1 = \alpha_2.$$

Hence $card(A) \le card(S) = card(B)$. Reversing the roles of A and B and repeating the argument gives $card(B) \le card(A)$ and hence $card(A) = card(B)$.

We may now define $\dim(H)$, the Hilbert space (or orthogonal) dimension of H, to be the cardinality of an orthonormal basis. This definition agrees with that of vector space (or Hamel) dimension when this dimension is finite, but not in general (again recall Exercise 3.7b). The difference between the two notions of dimension is that one allows for infinite linear combinations of basis elements (when such combinations converge), while the other permits only finite linear combinations (and no notion of convergence need be present). Specifically, in l^2 (square summable sequences) the standard unit vectors $\{e_i\}_{i=1}^{\infty}$ where e_i is a sequence with 1 in the ith component and 0 elsewhere form an orthonormal basis. But the $\{e_i\}$ are far from a vector space basis: There is certainly no way to express the sequence $\{2^{-i}\}_{i=1}^{\infty} \in l^2$ as a *finite* linear combination of the $\{e_i\}$.

EXERCISE 5.6 Prove that a Hilbert space H is *separable* (has a countable dense subset) if and only if $\dim(H)$ is countable. Hint: Use Gram–Schmidt and parts of Theorem 5.9.

□ OPERATORS AND THEIR ADJOINTS

Having considered the essential features of the structure of a Hilbert space H, we turn now to the more significant and involved matter of studying the structure of $\mathcal{B}(H)$, the bounded linear operators on H. We note immediately from past results that $\mathcal{B}(H)$ is not only a Banach space, but also has defined on it a multiplicative operation (operator composition), so that $\mathcal{B}(H)$ is an algebra of operators (indeed, as we shall see in Chapter 6, a Banach algebra). The continuity of this multiplicative operation results from the important inequality

$$\| ST \| \le \| S \| \, \| T \| \qquad (S, T \in \mathcal{B}(H)),$$

which we prove as follows:

$$\| ST \| = \sup_{\|x\|=1} \| STx \| \le \sup_{\|x\|=1} \| S \| \, \| Tx \| \qquad \text{(Theorem 3.3)}$$
$$= \| S \| \cdot \sup_{\|x\|=1} \| Tx \| = \| S \| \, \| T \|.$$

We now define a very important unary operation on $\mathcal{B}(H)$.

Given $T \in \mathcal{B}(H)$, the *adjoint operator* T^* of T is that unique member of $\mathcal{B}(H)$ determined by the identity

$$\langle Tx, y \rangle = \langle x, T^*y \rangle \quad \text{for all} \quad x, y \in H.$$

A unique T^* satisfying the above can always be found since, for each fixed $y \in H$, $\langle Tx, y \rangle$ is a continuous linear functional on H. Thus by Theorem 5.5 (or the self-conjugacy of H) there exists a unique $z \in H$ such that $\langle Tx, y \rangle = L_z(x) = \langle x, z \rangle$, and we define $T^*y = z$. The linearity of T^* follows since

$$\langle x, T^*(\alpha y_1 + y_2) \rangle = \langle Tx, \alpha y_1 + y_2 \rangle = \alpha^* \langle Tx, y_1 \rangle + \langle Tx, y_2 \rangle$$
$$= \alpha^* \langle x, T^*y_1 \rangle + \langle x, T^*y_2 \rangle = \langle x, \alpha T^*y_1 + T^*y_2 \rangle$$

for all $x \in X$, which implies $T^*(\alpha y_1 + y_2) = \alpha T^*y_1 + T^*y_2$ by Exercise 5.2c. The boundedness of T^* will be shown below. It should be noted that, as the notation suggests, this definition coincides with the definition of the adjoint of a bounded operator on a Banach space as presented at the end of Chapter 3, provided we use the identification of H with H^*. We shall see, however, that the conjugate linearity of this identification results in an alteration in one of the properties of the adjoint operation (compare Theorem 5.11a following with the result in the proof of Theorem 3.13c).

THEOREM 5.11 The operation $* : \mathcal{B}(H) \to \mathcal{B}(H)$ has the following properties for all $T, T_1, T_2 \in \mathcal{B}(H)$ and $\alpha_1, \alpha_2, \in \mathbf{C}$.

(a) $(\alpha_1 T_1 + \alpha_2 T_2)^* = \alpha_1^* T_1^* + \alpha_2^* T_2^*$.
(b) $(T_1 T_2)^* = T_2^* T_1^*$.
(c) $T^{**} = T$.
(d) $\| T^* \| = \| T \|$.
(e) $\| T^* T \| = \| T \|^2$.

□ **PROOF** Exercise 5.2c will be used without mention in (a), (b), and (c) below.

(a) For all $x, y \in H$,

$$
\begin{aligned}
\langle x, (\alpha_1 T_1 + \alpha_2 T_2)^* y \rangle &= \langle (\alpha_1 T_1 + \alpha_2 T_2) x, y \rangle \\
&= \alpha_1 \langle T_1 x, y \rangle + \alpha_2 \langle T_2 x, y \rangle \\
&= \alpha_1 \langle x, T_1^* y \rangle + \alpha_2 \langle x, T_2^* y \rangle \\
&= \langle x, (\alpha_1^* T_1^* + \alpha_2^* T_2^*) y \rangle .
\end{aligned}
$$

(b) $\langle x, (T_1 T_2)^* y \rangle = \langle T_1 T_2 x, y \rangle = \langle T_2 x, T_1^* y \rangle = \langle x, T_2^* T_1^* y \rangle$.
(c) $\langle x, (T^*)^* y \rangle = \langle T^* x, y \rangle = \langle y, T^* x \rangle^* = \langle Ty, x \rangle^* = \langle x, Ty \rangle$.
(d) By definition of the norm on $\mathcal{B}(H)$,

$$
\begin{aligned}
\| T^* \| \\
= \sup_{\|y\| = 1} \| T^* y \| &\leq \sup_{\substack{\|x\| = 1 \\ \|y\| = 1}} |\langle x, T^* y \rangle| \qquad (\text{let } x = T^* y / \| T^* y \|) \\
= \sup_{\substack{\|x\| = 1 \\ \|y\| = 1}} |\langle Tx, y \rangle| &\leq \sup_{\|x\| = 1} \| Tx \| \qquad (\text{Schwarz inequality}) \\
= \| T \| .
\end{aligned}
$$

Hence $\| T \| \geq \| T^* \|$, and the reverse inequality follows from (c) since $\| T^* \| \geq \| (T^*)^* \| = \| T \|$.

(e) By (d), $\| T^* T \| \leq \| T^* \| \, \| T \| = \| T \|^2$. Conversely,

$$\| Tx \|^2 = \langle Tx, Tx \rangle$$
$$= \langle T^*Tx, x \rangle \leq \| T^*Tx \| \, \| x \| \leq \| T^*T \| \, \| x \|^2.$$

Taking $\sup_{\|x\|=1}$ of the extreme sides of the above, we obtain $\| T \|^2 \leq \| T^*T \|$, which completes the proof.

If H is an n-dimensional Hilbert space, which we may think of as n-tuples of complex numbers with the usual inner product, it is useful to keep in mind that (relative to a given choice of basis) $\mathfrak{B}(H)$ is simply the algebra of n by n matrices with complex entries. For $T \in \mathfrak{B}(H)$, it turns out that T^* corresponds to the matrix that is the conjugate transpose of T (take the transpose of T and conjugate each entry). The useful and familiar notion of an *eigenvalue* of T ($\lambda \in \mathbf{C}$ such that $Tx = \lambda x$ for some nonzero *eigenvector* $x \in H$) has a natural generalization to the *spectrum* of T, which we define by

$$\sigma(T) = \{ \lambda \in \mathbf{C} : T - \lambda I \text{ is not invertible} \},$$

where I is the identity operator. Since the finite-dimensional result that a linear operator T is injective if and only if it is surjective does not hold in general, it follows that $\sigma(T)$ does indeed generalize the notion of eigenvalue (the notions coincide in the finite-dimensional case), but that $\lambda \in \sigma(T)$ need not be associated with an eigenvector x in the infinite-dimensional case (see Exercise 5.7 following). The spectrum of an operator on Hilbert space is of considerable practical and theoretical interest, and we introduce it here for this reason and as a warm-up for the further generalization of Chapter 6.

EXERCISE 5.7 Let l^2 be the Hilbert space of square summable sequences. We define the *shift operator* T on l^2 by

$$T(x_1, x_2, x_3, \ldots) = (0, x_1, x_2, x_3, \ldots).$$

a. Prove that the adjoint T^* of T is the reverse shift operator:

$$T^*(x_1, x_2, x_3, \ldots) = (x_2, x_3, \ldots).$$

b. Find the norms of T and T^* as members of $\mathfrak{B}(l^2)$.

c. Show that $0 \in \sigma(T)$ but that there is no associated (non-zero) eigenvector.

□ SELF-ADJOINT, NORMAL, UNITARY, AND PROJECTION OPERATORS

An operator $T \in \mathcal{B}(H)$ is defined to be *self-adjoint* if $T = T^*$. Such operators (or rather their unbounded counterparts) are of great importance in mathematical physics. One characterization of self-adjointness is given by

THEOREM 5.12 Given $T \in \mathcal{B}(H)$, then T is self-adjoint $\Leftrightarrow \langle Tx, x \rangle$ is real for all $x \in H$.

□ **PROOF** $\Rightarrow : T = T^* \Rightarrow \langle Tx, x \rangle = \langle x, Tx \rangle = \langle Tx, x \rangle^*$ for all $x \in H$. Hence $\langle Tx, x \rangle$ is real for all $x \in H$.
$\Leftarrow :$ Define $B(x) = \langle Tx, x \rangle$. Then

$$B(x + y) = B(x) + B(y) + \langle Ty, x \rangle + \langle Tx, y \rangle$$

and

$$B(x + iy) = B(x) + B(y) + i\langle Ty, x \rangle - i\langle Tx, y \rangle.$$

Since B is assumed to be real valued, we have for r and q real,

$$\langle Ty, x \rangle + \langle Tx, y \rangle = r,$$
$$\langle Ty, x \rangle - \langle Tx, y \rangle = iq.$$

Hence

$$\left. \begin{array}{l} 2\langle Ty, x \rangle = r + iq \\ 2\langle Tx, y \rangle = r - iq \end{array} \right\} \Rightarrow \langle Ty, x \rangle = \langle Tx, y \rangle^*.$$

Thus $\langle x, T^*y \rangle = \langle Tx, y \rangle = \langle Ty, x \rangle^* = \langle x, Ty \rangle$ for all $x, y \in H$, showing that $T = T^*$.

EXERCISE 5.8 Given $A \in \mathcal{B}(H)$ with $\langle Ax, x \rangle = 0$ for all $x \in H$, prove that $A = 0$. Hint: Show that both A and iA are self-adjoint and then deduce that A must be zero.

We now define some other special and important classes of operators. An operator $T \in \mathcal{B}(H)$ is *positive* if $\langle Tx, x \rangle \geq 0$ for all $x \in H$. An operator N is *normal* if N commutes with its adjoint, i.e., if $NN^* = N^*N$.

THEOREM 5.13 Given $\mathcal{N} \in \mathcal{B}(H)$, the following are equivalent:

a. $\mathcal{N}$ is normal.
b. $\mathcal{N} = \mathcal{N}_1 + i\mathcal{N}_2$ where $\mathcal{N}_1$ and $\mathcal{N}_2$ are self-adjoint and $\mathcal{N}_1\mathcal{N}_2 = \mathcal{N}_2\mathcal{N}_1$.
c. $\| \mathcal{N}x \| = \| \mathcal{N}^*x \|$ for all $x \in H$.

□ **PROOF** (a) $\Longrightarrow$ (b): Define $\mathcal{N}_1 = (\mathcal{N} + \mathcal{N}^*)/2$ and $\mathcal{N}_2 = (\mathcal{N} - \mathcal{N}^*)/2i$; it is readily checked that $\mathcal{N}_1$ and $\mathcal{N}_2$ are self-adjoint and commute. (Note the analogy between real and complex numbers and self-adjoint and normal operators.)

(b) $\Longrightarrow$ (c): Using the given decomposition of $\mathcal{N}$ along with $\mathcal{N}_1\mathcal{N}_2 = \mathcal{N}_2\mathcal{N}_1$,

$$\begin{aligned}
\| \mathcal{N}x \|^2 &= \langle \mathcal{N}x, \mathcal{N}x \rangle = \langle x, \mathcal{N}^*\mathcal{N}x \rangle = \langle x, (\mathcal{N}_1 - i\mathcal{N}_2)(\mathcal{N}_1 + i\mathcal{N}_2)x \rangle \\
&= \langle x, (\mathcal{N}_1^2 + \mathcal{N}_2^2)x \rangle = \langle x, (\mathcal{N}_1 + i\mathcal{N}_2)(\mathcal{N}_1 - i\mathcal{N}_2)x \rangle \\
&= \langle x, \mathcal{N}\mathcal{N}^*x \rangle = \langle \mathcal{N}^*x, \mathcal{N}^*x \rangle \\
&= \| \mathcal{N}^*x \|^2.
\end{aligned}$$

(c) $\Longrightarrow$ (a): For every $x \in H$ we have

$$\langle (\mathcal{N}\mathcal{N}^* - \mathcal{N}^*\mathcal{N})x, x \rangle = \langle \mathcal{N}\mathcal{N}^*x, x \rangle - \langle \mathcal{N}^*\mathcal{N}x, x \rangle$$
$$= \| \mathcal{N}^*x \|^2 - \| \mathcal{N}x \|^2 = 0.$$

Applying Exercise 5.8 to $\mathcal{N}\mathcal{N}^* - \mathcal{N}^*\mathcal{N}$, we conclude that $\mathcal{N}$ is normal.

The following result gives information on the spectrum of positive operators (and further suggests that they might more logically have been called nonnegative operators). The result will be useful (and further extended) at the end of Chapter 6.

THEOREM 5.14 Let T be a positive operator in $\mathcal{B}(H)$. Then

a. $T + I$ is invertible.
b. No negative real number can belong to $\sigma(T)$.

□ **PROOF** (a) Positivity of T says that $0 \leq \langle Tx, x \rangle$ for all $x \in H$. Injectivity of T follows since $(T + I)x = 0$ gives

$$\langle (T + I)x, x \rangle = 0 \Rightarrow 0 \leq \langle Tx, x \rangle = \langle -x, x \rangle = -\|x\|^2$$

$$\Rightarrow x = 0. \tag{1}$$

Surjectivity will follow if we can show that $M = \text{range}(T + I)$ is both dense and closed. Result (1) above can be applied to any $x \in M^\perp$, showing that $M^\perp = 0$ and hence that M is dense. Finally, for every $x \in H$, $\|(T + I)x\|^2 = \|Tx\|^2 + 2\langle Tx, x \rangle + \|x\|^2$, and hence $\|x\| \leq \|(T + I)x\|$. Thus Cauchy sequences $\{(T + I)x_n\}$ in M must come from Cauchy and hence convergent sequences $\{x_n\}$ in H, showing that M is complete and thereby closed in H.

(b) Suppose $r \in \sigma(T)$, $r < 0$. Then $T - rI$ fails to be invertible as does $-r^{-1}T + I$. Since $-r^{-1}T$ is positive whenever T is, this contradicts (a).

Given Hilbert spaces H and K, a linear transformation $T \in \mathcal{B}(H, K)$ is called *unitary* if T is an isometric ($\|Tx\| = \|x\|$) isomorphism of H *onto* K. It follows from the Hilbert space identity

$$\langle x, y \rangle = \sum_{n=1}^{4} i^n \|x + i^n y\|$$

stated at the beginning of the chapter that T is *inner product preserving* ($\langle Tx, Ty \rangle = \langle x, y \rangle$). Thus the existence of a unitary transformation between H and K says that these two spaces are essentially indistinguishable as far as their Hilbert space properties are concerned, and in this case H and K are called *unitarily equivalent*. A *unitary* operator is a unitary transformation from H onto itself.

THEOREM 5.15 Given $U \in \mathcal{B}(H)$, the following are equivalent:

(a) U is unitary.
(b) $UU^* = U^*U = I$ (so $U^* = U^{-1}$).
(c) $\langle Ux, Uy \rangle = \langle x, y \rangle$ for all $x, y \in H$, *and* U is surjective.

EXERCISE 5.9 Prove Theorem 5.15.

The final class of operators that we consider is the important class of *projection* operators. An operator $P \in \mathcal{B}(H)$ is a projection if $P^2 = P$.

As an example, let M be a closed subspace of H, and for each $x \in H$ define $P_M(x) = m$ where $m \in M$ is obtained from the unique direct sum decomposition $x = m + z$, $m \in M$ and $z \in M^\perp$ (recall $H = M \oplus M^\perp$). Clearly P_M is linear on H; and

$$P_M^2(x) = P_M(m) = m = P_M(x),$$

so $P_M^2 = P_M$. To show that $P_M \in \mathcal{B}(H)$, let $\|x\| = 1$ where $x = m + z$, $m \in M$ and $z \in M^\perp$. Then

$$\|x\|^2 = \|m + z\|^2 = \|m\|^2 + \|z\|^2 \geq \|m\|^2.$$

Hence $\|P_M x\|^2 = \|m\|^2 \leq \|x\|^2$, so $\|P_M\| \leq 1$ and $P_M \in \mathcal{B}(H)$. In fact if $M \neq \{0\}$, then $\|P_M\| = 1$ (why?). Thus P_M is a projection and it is called the *orthogonal projection* of H onto M. The next theorem singles out such orthogonal projections as a very important subclass, though nonorthogonal projections on H do exist in abundance.

THEOREM 5.16   Let $P \in \mathcal{B}(H)$ be a projection ($P^2 = P$). Then the following are equivalent:

a. P is positive.
b. P is self-adjoint.
c. P is normal.
d. P is the orthogonal projection on its range.

□   **PROOF**   (a) $\Rightarrow$ (b) and (b) $\Rightarrow$ (c) are immediate.

(c) $\Rightarrow$ (d): Letting $M = \text{range}(P)$, we first show that M is closed. Given $\{y_n\}_{n=1}^\infty$ in M with $y_n \to y$, we have $y_n = Px_n$, $x_n \in H$. Then

$$y_n = Px_n = P^2 x_n = Py_n \to Py,$$

so $y = Py \in M$ and hence M is closed. Now given $x \in H$ write $x = m + z$, $m \in M$ and $z \in M^\perp$. We must show that $Px = m$. Since $Px = Pm + Pz$, it suffices to show that $Pm = m$ and $Pz = 0$. Since $m \in M$, there exists $y \in H$ such that $m = Py$ and hence $Pm = P^2 y = Py = m$. By definition of M we have $Pz \in M$, and if we can also show that $Pz \in M^\perp$, we can conclude that $Pz = 0$. Accordingly, given any $m_1 \in M$, then $m_1 = Py_1$ and

$$\langle Pz, m_1 \rangle = \langle Pz, Py_1 \rangle = \langle z, P^* Py_1 \rangle = \langle z, PP^* y_1 \rangle = 0$$

since $P(P^*y_1) \in M$ and $z \in M^\perp$.

(d) $\Rightarrow$ (a): For any $x \in H$, write $x = m + z$, $m \in M$ and $z \in M^\perp$. Then

$$\langle Px, x \rangle = \langle m, m + z \rangle = \langle m, m \rangle + \langle m, z \rangle = \langle m, m \rangle \geq 0.$$

Hence P is positive and the proof is complete.

It should be noted that there is a natural one-to-one correspondence between projection operators P and direct sum decompositions $H = M \oplus N$, M and N closed. Indeed, given P define $M = \text{range}(P)$ and $N = \text{range}(I - P)$; and given $H = M \oplus N$, define P as was done for the orthogonal projection but using N instead of $M^\perp$. The orthogonal projections are precisely those that arise when $N = M^\perp$, and these are generally the projections of interest in Hilbert space theory.

EXERCISE 5.10   Let I be an integral on a linear lattice of functions defined on a set S. Let $L^2(I)$ be the complex Hilbert space obtained from I, with inner product $\langle f, g \rangle = I(fg^*)$. Given $f \in L^\infty(I)$, the Banach space of (essentially) bounded Baire functions with the (essential) sup norm, define the multiplication operator $M_f : L^2(I) \to L^2(I)$ by $M_f(g) = fg$.

a. Prove that $M_f \in \mathcal{B}(L^2(I))$ and $\|M_f\| = \|f\|_\infty$. Hint: $\|M_f\| \leq \|f\|_\infty$ is fairly direct, but you may wish to settle for a plausibility argument that $\|M_f\| = \|f\|_\infty$.

b. Prove that M_f is a normal operator on $L^2(I)$ and determine $(M_f)^*$.

c. Argue that if the values of f are (except on a set of measure zero) real, nonnegative, of modulus 1, either 0 or 1, then M_f is respectively self-adjoint, positive, unitary, a projection.

Recalling our matrix interpretation of operators on finite-dimensional Hilbert space and of their adjoints, we can now make the following observations. The self-adjoint operators correspond to matrices that are conjugate symmetric (thus real symmetric matrices are self-adjoint) and the unitary operators correspond to matrices whose row vectors (or column vectors) form an orthonormal basis. The unitary (or orthogonal) matrices are precisely those matrices that arise in changing from one orthonormal basis to another, and a fundamental result of matrix theory states that a normal matrix N can be viewed under some orthonormal basis change (with unitary operator U) as a diagonal matrix D: thus $N = UDU^{-1}$. The diagonal entries in D are then just the spectrum or eigenvalues of N. One of the many avenues of generalization of this important result will be a principal goal of the next chapter.

UNBOUNDED OPERATORS AND QUANTUM MECHANICS

We complete this chapter by attempting to relate some of the preceding ideas to quantum mechanics, which provided the impetus for much of the Hilbert space theory. We cannot expect to deal very generally or satisfactorily with the important philosophical and much debated subtleties of the formalism of quantum mechanics without requiring more space and knowledge of physics than would be reasonable in this undertaking. Nevertheless, it is hoped that the spirit of the intellectual triumph of the late 1920s which resulted in quantum mechanics can be conveyed by utilizing the considerable mathematical machinery that we have developed and by restricting ourselves to simple special cases.

Physics in the early twentieth century was in a state of great excitement and confusion. Einstein's theories of special and general relativity had initiated a break with classical Newtonian physics and had "proven" themselves by resolving numerous previously unexplained results and by successfully predicting new results. The determinism of Newtonian physics still remained as did many unresolved and seemingly contradictory experimental facts. That a deterministic view of the universe must give way to a description of particle behavior according to a probability distribution is a fundamental tenet of quantum mechanics and, despite Einstein's fervent belief that "God does not play dice with the world," this view of a universe behaving and evolving according to the laws of chance continues to provide the most satisfactory model to date of "the way things are." In what follows we outline (in a one-dimensional nonrelativistic setting) the way in which Hilbert space theory helps to formalize this view.

A *state* ψ of a particle constrained to one dimension in a physical system is treated as a (Lebesgue) square summable complex-valued function on $\mathbf{R}$, i.e., as a member of the Hilbert space $L^2(\mathbf{R})$. If S is a region (or a Lebesgue measurable subset) of $\mathbf{R}$, then $\int_S |\psi|^2$ represents the probability that a particle in state ψ is in the region S. Thus we are compelled to require that

$$\|\psi\|^2 = \langle \psi, \psi \rangle = \int_{\mathbf{R}} |\psi|^2 = 1$$

(the particle has probability 1 of being somewhere on $\mathbf{R}$). This results in an identification between states of the system and rays in $L^2(\mathbf{R})$ (one-dimensional subspaces); and any norm-1 representative from a ray provides a so-called probability density function for the state to which it corresponds. In order to ascertain the physical interpretation of operators H on $L^2(\mathbf{R})$ we intersperse a few basic ideas from probability theory.

Given a quantity that takes on real values in some probabilistic fashion (more formally, a *random variable*), its *probability density function* is a function $f: \mathbf{R} \to \mathbf{R}$ such that $\int_{x_1}^{x_2} f(x)\, dx$ is the probability that the quantity is between x_1 and x_2. Thus $|\psi|^2$ above is a probability density function corresponding to the random variable whose values are locations in $\mathbf{R}$ of a particle in state ψ. With a probability density function f arising from a random variable one associates an *expectation* or *expected value* E_f defined by

$$E_f = \int_{\mathbf{R}} x \cdot f(x)\, dx,$$

which can be thought of as an average value of the random variable. The *variance* or "error" D_f of f (or of its generating random variable) is defined by

$$D_f = \int_{\mathbf{R}} (x - E_f)^2 f(x)\, dx.$$

The variance D_f provides a measure of how much the random variable deviates from its expected value, and $(D_f)^{1/2}$ is called the *standard deviation* for the random variable. All these formulas are natural continuous analogues of the more familiar summation formulas arising from discrete probabilistic situations.

Returning now to $L^2(\mathbf{R})$ and our particle, we regard various properties or *observables* of the particle as operators on $L^2(\mathbf{R})$ in the following sense: If A is the observable, then

$$E_\psi(A) = \langle A\psi, \psi \rangle$$

represents the expected value of A, given an initial state ψ. Important examples of such observables are the position, the momentum, and the energy of a particle. The fact that the expected values of the observables must be real suggests (Theorem 5.12) that observables should be associated with *self-adjoint* operators.

Note that the expected value of the position of a particle in state ψ is

$$E_\psi = \int_{\mathbf{R}} x \mid \psi(x) \mid^2 dx = \int_{\mathbf{R}} x\psi(x)\psi^*(x) \, dx.$$

If we let Q denote the position observable, then

$$E_\psi(Q) = \langle Q\psi, \psi \rangle = \int_{\mathbf{R}} Q\psi(x)\psi^*(x) \, dx,$$

and we see a compelling reason for defining the *position operator* Q on $L^2(\mathbf{R})$ by

$$(Q\psi)(x) = x\psi(x).$$

A more involved motivational argument, which we omit, suggests defining the *momentum operator* P on $L^2(\mathbf{R})$ by

$$P = \frac{h}{2\pi i} \frac{d}{dx},$$

where $H = 6.625 \times 10^{-34}$ joule · sec is Planck's constant. Ignoring for the moment the fact that P and Q are not defined everywhere on $L^2(\mathbf{R})$, we note that both are linear and (Problem 5.6) both satisfy the inner product definition of self-adjoint whenever the inner product is defined.

In analogy with our definition of variance above, we may define, for any self-adjoint operator A,

$$\begin{aligned} D_\psi(A) &= \| (A - E_\psi(A)I)\psi \|^2 \\ &= \langle (A - E_\psi(A)I)\psi, (A - E_\psi(A)I)\psi \rangle \\ &= \int_{\mathbf{R}} (A - E_\psi(A)I)^2 \psi(x)\psi^*(x) \, dx. \end{aligned}$$

After all this hard work a common formulation of the famous uncertainty relation of Heisenberg will be seen to emerge as a result of

LEMMA 5.17 If A and B are self-adjoint operators on a Hilbert space H and $\psi \in H$, then $D_\psi(A)D_\psi(B) \geq \frac{1}{4} \mid E_\psi(AB - BA) \mid^2$.

□ **PROOF**

$$
\begin{aligned}
| E\psi(AB - BA)|^2 &= |\langle(AB - BA)\psi,\psi\rangle|^2 \\
&= |\langle AB\psi,\psi\rangle - \langle BA\psi,\psi\rangle|^2 \\
&= |\langle AB\psi,\psi\rangle - \langle\psi,AB\psi\rangle|^2 \\
&= |\langle AB\psi,\psi\rangle - \langle AB\psi,\psi\rangle^*|^2 \\
&= (2\mathrm{Im}\langle AB\psi,\psi\rangle)^2
\end{aligned}
$$

(Im denotes the imaginary part.) Now noting that for any $a, b \in \mathbf{R}$,

$$
AB - BA = (A - aI)(B - bI) - (B - bI)(A - aI),
$$

and letting $a = E_\psi(A)$ and $b = E_\psi(B)$, we conclude that

$$
\begin{aligned}
\tfrac{1}{4}| E_\psi(AB - BA)|^2 &= \tfrac{1}{4}| E_\psi((A - E_\psi(A)I)(B - E_\psi(B)I) \\
&\quad - (B - E_\psi(B)I)(A - E_\psi(A)I))|^2 \\
&= (\mathrm{Im}\langle(A - E_\psi(A)I)(B - E_\psi(B)I)\psi,\psi\rangle)^2 \\
&= (\mathrm{Im}\langle(A - E_\psi(A)I)\psi,(B - E_\psi(B)I)\psi\rangle)^2 \\
&\leq \|(A - E_\psi(A)I)\psi\|^2\|(B - E_\psi(B)I)\psi\|^2 \\
&= D_\psi(A)D_\psi(B),
\end{aligned}
$$

where self-adjointness and Schwarz's inequality have been used above.

Replacing A by the momentum operator P and B by the position operation Q on $L^2(\mathbf{R})$, we note that

$$
\begin{aligned}
(PQ - QP)\psi(x) &= PQ\psi(x) - QP\psi(x) \\
&= \frac{h}{2\pi i}\frac{d}{dx}(x\psi(x)) - x \cdot \frac{d\psi(x)}{dx} \\
&= \frac{h}{2\pi i}\psi(x).
\end{aligned}
$$

Thus

$$
PQ - QP = \frac{h}{2\pi i} I.
$$

Using this fact, noting that the variances $D_\psi(P)$ and $D_\psi(Q)$ are frequently replaced in physics by $(\Delta p)^2$ and $(\Delta x)^2$ (so Δp and Δx

are "standard deviations"), and taking square roots in the statement of Lemma 5.17, we obtain for any state ψ

$$\Delta p \cdot \Delta x \geq \frac{1}{2} \mid E_\psi \left(\frac{h}{2\pi i} I \right) \mid = \frac{1}{2} \mid \left\langle \frac{h}{2\pi i} \psi, \psi \right\rangle \mid = \frac{h}{4\pi} \parallel \psi \parallel^2 = \frac{h}{4\pi}.$$

Thus $\Delta p \cdot \Delta x \geq h/(4\pi)$, which quantifies the *Heisenberg uncertainty principle* that the position and complementary momentum of a particle cannot be, simultaneously determined with complete precision.

It should now (perhaps belatedly) be pointed out that the operators P and Q we have been discussing are not bounded operators in our usual sense (though Lemma 5.17 is still valid for vectors at which all operators in question are defined). Indeed neither P nor Q can be defined on all of $L^2(\mathbf{R})$ and it can be shown that P and Q are discontinuous at some (and hence all) points for which they are defined. This suggests that our study of $\mathfrak{B}(H)$ is inadequate for the purposes of physics and that we need to extend some of our ideas to the case of "unbounded" operators. If we accept the importance (in physics) of operators A and B for which $AB - BA = \gamma I$ ($\gamma \in \mathbf{C}$ and $\gamma \neq 0$) as indicated by the importance of P and Q, the physical necessity of considering unbounded operators is brought home most emphatically by the following elegant result.

THEOREM 5.18   **Wintner as Proved by Wielandt**
There do not exist $A, B \in \mathfrak{B}(H)$ such that $AB - BA = \gamma I$, $\gamma \in \mathbf{C}$ and $\gamma \neq 0$.

□   **PROOF**   It suffices to consider the case $\gamma = 1$ (why?), which we do. Suppose, on the contrary, that there exist $A, B \in \mathfrak{B}(H)$ such that $I = AB - BA$. An induction argument will show that

$$nB^{n-1} = AB^n - B^n A \qquad (n = 1, 2, \ldots). \tag{1}$$

Indeed the $n = 1$ case is simply the assumed result involving A and B, and assuming the result holds a general n, we have

$$(n + 1)B^n = nB^{n-1}B + B^n I$$
$$= (AB^n - B^n A)B + B^n(AB - BA)$$

$$= AB^{n+1} - B^{n+1}A,$$

establishing the induction result. Applying the triangle inequality and the fact that $\|ST\| \leq \|S\| \, \|T\|$ to (1), we obtain

$$n\|B^{n-1}\| \leq 2\|A\| \, \|B\| \, \|B^{n-1}\| \qquad (n = 1,2,\ldots).$$

This result requires that $\|B^n\| = 0$ for *some* n since otherwise we would have $n \leq 2\|A\| \, \|B\|$ for every n which is impossible under the assumption that A and B are bounded. Finally, using (1) repeatedly,

$$\|B^n\| = 0 \Rightarrow B^n = 0 \Rightarrow B^{n-1} = 0 \Rightarrow \cdots \Rightarrow B = 0 \Rightarrow I = 0,$$

which is untenable (except in zero-dimensional Hilbert space), establishes our contradiction, and shows that such bounded operators cannot exist.

To treat unbounded operators we first restrict ourselves to those not necessarily bounded linear operators having two special properties. From the closed graph theorem we obtained the result that an (everywhere defined) operator is bounded if and only if its graph is closed. We now define a not necessarily everywhere defined operator T to be *closed* if the graph of T is closed, i.e., if

$$x_n \in \text{domain}(T), \qquad x_n \to x, \qquad Tx_n \to y$$

$$\Rightarrow \quad x \in \text{domain}(T) \quad \text{and} \quad Tx = y.$$

The (possibly) unbounded operators we wish to consider are those operators (linear maps from a subspace of H to H) that are *closed* and whose domains are *dense* in H.

If T is such a closed, densely defined operator we now show that an adjoint operation $*$ is still defined on T. We proceed as before, considering for each fixed $y \in H$ the linear functional $\langle Tx, y \rangle$ defined for $x \in \text{domain}(T)$. Then $\text{domain}(T^*)$ will be precisely those $y \in H$ for which there exists $z \in H$ such that $\langle Tx, y \rangle = \langle x, z \rangle$ for all $x \in \text{domain}(T)$. The fact that T is densely defined guarantees the uniqueness of z since $\langle Tx, y \rangle = \langle x, z_1 \rangle = \langle x, z_2 \rangle$ for all $x \in \text{domain}(T)$ implies $\langle x, z_1 - z_2 \rangle = 0$ for all x on a dense set, which in turn implies that $z_1 = z_2$. Thus for $y \in \text{domain}(T^*)$ we define T^*y to be that unique z such that $\langle Tx, y \rangle = \langle x, z \rangle$ for all $x \in \text{domain}(T)$.

It can be readily verified that T^* is linear and closed and that *if T^{**} is well defined* (i.e., if T^* is densely defined), then T^{**} is an extension of T. If T^* is an extension of T, then T is called *symmetric* or *Hermitian*. We define a densely defined operator to be *self-adjoint* if, as in the bounded case, $T = T^*$ by which we mean that domain$(T) = $ domain(T^*) and that T and T^* act identically on this domain. Note that since T^* is always closed, a necessary condition for self-adjointness is that T be closed.

To illustrate the above concepts (omitting proofs), consider the real Hilbert space $H = L^2(0, \infty)$ and the differentiation operator D defined by $DF = f'$ (taking liberty with equivalence classes). Thus

$$\text{domain}(D) = \{f \in H : f' \text{ exists and } \int_0^\infty |f'|^2 < \infty\}.$$

Note that D is unbounded by considering $f_k(t) = e^{-kt}$, $k = 1, 2, \ldots$, for then $f'_k(t) = -ke^{-kt}$, f_k and $f'_k \in H$ for all $k = 1, 2, \ldots$, and $\|Df_k\| = k\|f_k\|$. Hence there is no constant K such that $\|Df\| \leq K\|f\|$ for all $f \in$ domain(D) and D is not bounded.

Accepting the fact that domain(D) is dense in H, we now examine D^*. Using integration by parts and some license with limits.

$$\langle Df, g \rangle = \int_0^\infty f'(t)g(t)\,dt = (fg)(t)\bigg|_0^\infty - \int_0^\infty f(t)g'(t)\,dt$$
$$= -\lim_{t \to 0} f(t)g(t) + \langle f, -Dg \rangle \qquad (f \in \text{domain}(D)).$$

The conclusion is that if we define

$$\text{domain}(D^*) = \{g \in H : g \in \text{domain}(D) \text{ and } \lim_{t \to 0} g(t) = 0\};$$

then, for $g \in$ domain(D^*), $D^*g = -Dg$. It follows that for $g \in$ domain(D^*),

$$\left(\frac{h}{2\pi i} D\right)^* g = \left(\frac{h}{2\pi i} D\right)g,$$

but $(h/2\pi i)D$ is *not* self-adjoint since it has a larger domain than its adjoint.

This is to be contrasted (Problem 5.6) with the situation of the very closely related operator $P = (h/2\pi i)(d/dx)$ on $L^2(\mathbf{R})$, which is self-adjoint. Thus the choice of a domain for the operator is crucial to questions about the nature of its adjoint. Unbounded operators play an essential role in much of the work in differential equations and in quantum mechanics, and the above, it is hoped, indicates some of the problems and challenges that may arise.

□ REMARKS

For a novel treatment of Hilbert space theory, Halmos' *A Hilbert Space Problem Book* [14] is highly recommended. The formulation, solution, and discussion of 199 problems provides the strongly motivated reader with a most enjoyable and effective method of mastering most of the theory.

We have already mentioned (in the proof of Theorem 5.13, (a) ⟹ (b)) the analogy between self-adjoint versus normal operators and real versus complex numbers. This analogy is strengthened and extended by the fact that self-adjoint operators have real spectrum, positive operators have nonnegative spectrum, unitary operators have spectrum sitting on the unit circumference in $\mathbf{C}$, and projections have spectrum that is a subset of $\{0,1\}$. Problem 5.4 deals with a few of these results, and the rest will follow readily from the spectral theory of Chapter 6.

Problem 5.3 introduces a natural partial order relation on the self-adjoint operators and suggests that the orthogonal projections even have a complete lattice structure (closure under least upper bounds and greatest lower bounds) with respect to this ordering. More recent formulations of quantum mechanics have these projections playing the role of physical questions with yes or no answers, and the lattice structure plays an important role in this development. At a more elementary level, Gillespie's book [15] provides a helpful introduction to some of the physical background of quantum mechanics and gives additional details of the role of the Hilbert space formalsim. See Cline's book [16] for a nontechnical, biographical and historical treatment of the remarkable developments of physics in the first three decades of the twentieth century.

Our discussion of unbounded operators was meant to motivate their necessity and to show how to get started. For a thorough treatment, see Goldberg's book [14]. The fact that these operators

appear to be physically indispensable and yet are mathematically
so much less tractable and appealing than the friendly bounded
operators would appear to be very unfortunate. The situation is
alleviated considerably by the fact that there is a natural way to
identify an unbounded, self-adjoint operator with a (one-param-
eter) group of unitary operators. Roughly speaking, the trick is to
multiply by any purely imaginary number and then "exponenti-
ate" (see Problem 5.7). These unitary groups (and, more generally, semigroups) of operators enable problems with unbounded
operators to be reduced to questions about bounded operators
and are also of considerable importance as "time-evolution operators" of a physical system. Groups and semigroups of operators are treated concisely in Dunford and Schwartz [9, Chapter VIII], and most thoroughly in Hille and Phillips' book [18].

☐ **PROBLEMS**

1. Prove that any Hilbert space H is unitarily equivalent to an L^2
   space of square-summable functions on some set S. Hint: Pick
   an orthonormal basis $\{e_\alpha\}$ for H and define S to be an index set
   for this basis (S is a set whose cardinality coincides with that of
   $\{e_\alpha\}$). Define

   $$L^2 = \{f : S \to \mathbf{C} : f(s) = 0 \quad \text{for all but countably many } s \text{ and}$$
   $$\sum_{s \in S} |f(s)|^2 < \infty\}.$$

   Show that L^2 can be regarded as a Hilbert space, choose a natural orthonormal basis for L^2, and demonstrate that H and L^2
   are unitarily equivalent by matching up their orthonormal
   bases in a natural way.

2. a. Given $T \in \mathcal{B}(H)$ and T self-adjoint, prove $T^2 x = 0 \Rightarrow$
   $Tx = 0$.
   b. Extend the result of (a) to the case when T is normal.
   Hint: T normal $\Rightarrow \|Ty\| = \|T^*y\|$ for all $y \in H$. Let $y = Tx$.

3. If S and T are self-adjoint operators on H define $S \leq T$ to mean
   $\langle Sx, x \rangle \leq \langle Tx, x \rangle$ for all $x \in H$.
   a. Prove that $\leq$ is a partial order relation on the set of self-
   adjoint operators.

b. Given orthogonal projections P_M and P_N on H, prove that

$$P_M \leq P_N \iff \|P_M x\| \leq \|P_N x\| \quad \text{for all} \quad x \in H \iff M \subseteq N.$$

c. Show that any collection $\{P_\alpha\}$ of orthogonal projections has a lub and a glb; this makes the orthogonal projections into a *complete* lattice. Hint: If M_α is the range of P_α, $\cap_\alpha M_\alpha$ provides the range of a glb and $(\cap_\alpha (M_\alpha)^\perp)^\perp$ provides the range of a lub.

4. a. Prove that every projection operator P (orthogonal or otherwise) which is not 0 or I has $\sigma(P) = \{0,1\}$. Hint: Show that when $\lambda \neq \lambda^2$, a multiple of $P + (\lambda - 1)I$ will serve as inverse to $P - \lambda I$.

b. Prove T self-adjoint and $\lambda \notin \mathbf{R} \Rightarrow T - \lambda I$ injective. It can also be shown (Chapter 6) that $T - \lambda I$ is surjective and hence (open mapping theorem) invertible. Thus T self-adjoint $\Rightarrow \sigma(T) \subseteq \mathbf{R}$.

5. a. Given a subset U of C, define $U^* = \{u^* \in \mathbf{C} : u \in U\}$. Prove for any $T \in \mathfrak{B}(H)$ that $\sigma(T^*) = (\sigma(T))^*$.

b. Prove that $T \in \mathfrak{B}(H)$ and $|\lambda| > \|T\| \Rightarrow \lambda \notin \sigma(T)$. Hint: Argue that $\lambda^{-1}\sum_{k=0}^{\infty}(T/\lambda)^k$ is in $\mathfrak{B}(H)$ and that it is inverse to $\lambda(I - T/\lambda)$.

c. Let T be the shift operator of Exercise 5.7. Prove that $\sigma(T) = \{z \in \mathbf{C} : |z| \leq 1\}$. Hint: It is easier to work with T^*.

6. a. Let $P = (h/2\pi i)(d/dx)$ denote the momentum operator on $L^2(\mathbf{R})$ with

domain $(P) = \{f \in L^2(\mathbf{R}) : Pf \text{ exists and } Pf \in L^2(\mathbf{R})\}$.

Show using integration by parts that $\langle Pf, g \rangle = \langle f, Pg \rangle$ for all $f, g \in \text{domain}(P)$, thus suggesting that P is self-adjoint. (A formal proof would have to be more precise about domain (P) and the fact that P is closed.)

b. Let Q denote the position operator on $L^2(\mathbf{R}) : Qf(x) = xf(x)$, where

domain $(Q) = \{f \in L^2(\mathbf{R}) : \int_{\mathbf{R}} |xf(x)|^2 \, dx < \infty\}$.

Show that Q is unbounded by exhibiting a sequence $\{f_n\}_{n=1}^{\infty}$ in domain (Q) such that $\|f_n\| = 1$ for all n, but $\|Qf_n\| \to \infty$.

c. Prove that $\langle Qf, g \rangle = \langle f, Qg \rangle$ for all $f, g \in \text{domain}(Q)$.

7. Let $H = L^2(\mathbf{R})$, and for each real number t define an operator $U(t)$ on $L^2(\mathbf{R})$ by $(U(t)f)(x) = f(x + t)$.

a. Prove that for each $t \in \mathbf{R}$, $U(t)$ is a unitary operator on $L^2(\mathbf{R})$.

b. Show that $\{U(t)\}_{t \in \mathbf{R}}$ is isomorphic to the group $\mathbf{R}$ in the sense that $U(t_1 + t_2) = U(t_1) \cdot U(t_2)$ for all $t_1, t_2 \in \mathbf{R}$.

c. Argue that $dU(t)/dt \big|_{t=0} = D = d/dx$, the (unbounded differentiation operator on $L^2(\mathbf{R})$ with domain

$$\left\{ f \in L^2(\mathbf{R}) : \frac{df}{dx} \quad \text{exists and} \quad \frac{df}{dx} \in L^2(\mathbf{R}) \right\}.$$

d. Present plausibility arguments for writing $U(t) = e^{tD}$, thereby illustrating the process of identifying certain unbounded operators with a group of unitary operators.

Commutative
Banach Algebras
and a Spectral Theorem

6

□ DEFINITION AND EXAMPLES

With the space $\mathcal{B}(H)$ of bounded operators on a Hilbert space very much in mind, we investigate in this chapter some aspects of the theory of Banach algebras. Besides providing a natural area of interplay for algebra, analysis, and topology, this topic will bring together a surprising number of the major results and ideas of preceding chapters. As an added bonus, the theory will provide a neat proof of one version of the spectral theorem for bounded normal operators.

We work throughout with a *complex Banach algebra with identity*, which we denote by A. Thus A is a Banach space on which is defined a "multiplicative" operation satisfying for all x, y, $z \in A$ and $\alpha \in \mathbf{C}$:

(a) $x(yz) = (xy)z$.
(b) $x(y + z) = xy + xz$ and $(x + y)z = xz + yz$.
(c) $\alpha(xy) = (\alpha x)y = x(\alpha y)$.
(d) $\|xy\| \leq \|x\| \, \|y\|$.
(e) There exists a multiplicative identity in A, call it 1, with $\|1\| = 1$.

EXERCISE 6.1 Prove that the multiplication operation on a Banach algebra is continuous.

We will eventually restrict ourselves to a commutative multiplication with the justification that one fundamental result we seek (the Gelfand representation theorem) does not obtain in the noncommutative case. The requirement of an identity for A, while considerably simplifying the discussion, is not crucial since a Banach algebra can always be imbedded in a larger one with identity (see Problem 6.1). Also the assumption that $\|1\| = 1$ is avoidable since an equivalent norm (recall Exercise 3.3) can always be found for which this is the case [13, p. 48].

A *Banach subalgebra* of a Banach algebra A is defined as a *closed* subalgebra of A containing the identity. We now present three general types of examples of Banach algebras and subalgebras, not necessarily commutative.

□ **EXAMPLE 1**

Let S be a compact Hausdorff space and let $\mathcal{C}(S)$ be the Banach space of continuous, complex-valued functions on S, endowed with the sup norm. Then $\mathcal{C}(S)$ is also closed under *pointwise* multiplication of functions and is readily seen to be a commutative algebra with identity. This example can be generalized by letting S be any topological space and requiring the functions on S to also be bounded. An important Banach subalgebra is obtained by taking S to be $\bar{D}$, the closed unit disk in $\mathbf{C}$, and by defining $\mathcal{A}(\bar{D})$ to be those members of $\mathcal{C}(\bar{D})$ that are analytic on the open disk D. (This must be distinguished from $\mathcal{A}(D)$, the analytic functions on D, which cannot be made into a Banach algebra—see Problem 6.2.) Algebras of functions whose multiplication is pointwise are called (not surprisingly) *function algebras*.

□ **EXAMPLE 2**

If X is a Banach space, the collection $\mathcal{B}(X)$ of all bounded operators on X is a Banach algebra whose multiplication is composition of operators. Recall that $\mathcal{B}(X)$ is not commutative (unless X is one dimensional), but $\mathcal{B}(X)$ does have an identity. If $X = H$, a Hilbert space, and if N is a normal operator on H, we shall have occasion to consider the smallest Banach subalgebra of $\mathcal{B}(H)$ containing N and N^*. This will be seen to be the closure in $\mathcal{B}(H)$ of all polynomials in N and N^* and hence a commutative Banach (sub)algebra. The above represent examples from the class of *operator algebras*.

□ **EXAMPLE 3**

Given the Lebesgue intergral on $\mathbf{R}$, the set $L^1(\mathbf{R})$ has been shown to be a Banach space. If multiplication of f and g in $L^1(\mathbf{R})$ is performed by *convolution*: $f * g(x) = \int_{\mathbf{R}} f(x - y) g(y) \, dy$, it can be shown that $f * g$ is in $L^1(\mathbf{R})$ and that $L^1(\mathbf{R})$ is a commutative Banach algebra (without identity). Algebras obtained in this manner are called *convolution algebras*. In general **R** can be replaced by a locally compact group G (and its Haar integral) in which case $L^1(G)$ will be commutative if and only if G is abelian, and $L^1(G)$ will have an identity if and only if G is discrete [3, p. 123].

EXERCISE 6.2   a. Show that the Banach space $L^1(\mathbf{R})$ of example 3 is indeed a commutative Banach algebra. Hint: Commutativity requires a change of variable under the integral sign.

b. Relate the assertion that $L^1(\mathbf{R})$ has no identity to the assertion of Chapter 3 that the Dirac δ distribution is not a distribution function.

Our treatment, when it becomes specific, will deal primarily with the algebras of Examples 1 and 2, though unless otherwise stated all results will apply to any (not necessarily commutative) Banach algebra with identity. It is strongly recommended that the reader keep in mind at frequent intervals the algebra $\mathcal{B}(H)$, which we have treated in some detail in Chapter 5.

□ **SPECTRUM AND RESOLVENT**

Letting A be a Banach algebra with identity, we decompose A into the set G of *regular* or *invertible* elements,

$$G = \{x \in A : \text{there exists } x^{-1} \in A \text{ such that } xx^{-1} = x^{-1}x = 1\},$$

and the complementary set S of *singular* or *noninvertible* elements. Note that G is a (multiplicative) group with identity 1.

THEOREM 6.1   Let A be a Banach algebra with identity. Then

a. $\|x - 1\| < 1 \Longrightarrow x \in G$ and $x^{-1} = \sum_{i=0}^{\infty}(1 - x)^i$.

b. G is an open subset of A and hence S is closed.

□ **PROOF** (a) Letting $r = \|x - 1\| < 1$, we note that $\{\sum_{i=0}^{n}(1 - x)^i\}_{n=1}^{\infty}$ is a Cauchy sequence in A since $\|(1 - x)^n\| \leq \|1 - x\|^n = r^n$. The completeness of A then ensures that this sequence must converge to a member of A, which we naturally denote by $\sum_{i=0}^{\infty}(1 - x)^i$. Then

$$x \sum_{i=0}^{\infty} (1 - x)^i = (1 - (1 - x)) \sum_{i=0}^{\infty} (1 - x)^i$$

$$= \sum_{i=0}^{\infty} (1 - x)^i - \sum_{i=1}^{\infty} (1 - x)^i = 1.$$

A similar argument shows that $(\sum_{i=0}^{\infty}(1 - x)^i)x = 1$. We conclude that $x \in G$ and $x^{-1} = \sum_{i=0}^{\infty}(1 - x)^i$.

(b) Given $x_0 \in G$, choose *any* $x \in A$ such that $\|x - x_0\| < \|x_0^{-1}\|^{-1}$. Then

$$\|x_0^{-1}x - 1\| = \|x_0^{-1}(x - x_0)\| \leq \|x_0^{-1}\| \|x - x_0\| < 1,$$

so by (a) we have $x_0^{-1}x \in G$. Since G is a group, it then follows that $x = x_0(x_0^{-1}x) \in G$, and we have shown that the open disk of radius $\|x_0^{-1}\|^{-1}$ about x_0 is contained in G, so G is open.

The *spectrum* $\sigma(x)$ of $x \in A$ is defined by

$$\sigma(x) = \{\lambda \in \mathbf{C} : x - \lambda 1 \in S\}.$$

We have already remarked that the spectrum of an operator in the Banach algebra $\mathfrak{B}(H)$ is an important idea and a natural generalization of the set of eigenvalues of an operator (or matrix relative to choice of basis) in the finite-dimensional case.

EXERCISE 6.3 Let $\mathfrak{C}(\mathbf{R})$ be the Banach algebra of bounded continuous functions on $\mathbf{R}$ (sup norm).

a. Given $f \in \mathfrak{C}(\mathbf{R})$ defined by $f(t) = \sin(t)$, find $\sigma(f)$.

b. Generalize your reasoning in (a) to describe $\sigma(f)$ for an arbitrary $f \in \mathfrak{C}(\mathbf{R})$ by means of a more familiar set theoretic concept. Conclude that $\sigma(f)$ is always a nonempty subset of $\mathbf{C}$ and that $\sigma(f) = \{0\} \implies f = 0$.

c. Show that the final implication in (b) does not hold in the

Banach algebra of 2 by 2 (complex) matrices by considering

$$B = \begin{bmatrix} 0 & 1 \\ 0 & 0 \end{bmatrix}.$$

The *resolvent set* $\rho(x)$ of $x \in A$ is the complement in $\mathbf{C}$ of $\sigma(x)$, and the *resolvent* (function) $R_x : \rho(x) \rightarrow A$ for x is defined by

$$R_x(\lambda) = (x - \lambda 1)^{-1}.$$

THEOREM 6.2 For each $x \in A$, $\sigma(x)$ is a compact subset of $\mathbf{C}$ and hence $\rho(x)$ is open in $\mathbf{C}$.

□ **PROOF** We show that $\sigma(x)$ is bounded and closed in $\mathbf{C}$. Boundedness will follow from the fact that $\lambda \in \sigma(x) \Rightarrow |\lambda| \le \|x\|$. Indeed

$$|\lambda| > \|x\| \Rightarrow \|(1 - x/\lambda) - 1\| = \|x/\lambda\| < 1$$
$$\Rightarrow 1 - x/\lambda \in G \quad (\text{Theorem 6.1a})$$
$$\Rightarrow x - \lambda 1 \in G \Rightarrow \lambda \notin \sigma(x).$$

Closedness follows since $\lambda_n \in \sigma(x)$, $\lambda_n \rightarrow \lambda \Rightarrow x - \lambda_n 1 \in S$. Since S is closed (Theorem 6.1b) we conclude that $x - \lambda 1 \in S$, so $\lambda \in \sigma(x)$. Thus $\sigma(x)$ is compact and its complement $\rho(x)$ is open.

LEMMA 6.3 Given $\lambda, \mu \in \rho(x)$, the resolvent function R_x satisfies the *resolvent equation*

$$R_x(\lambda) - R_x(\mu) = (\lambda - \mu) R_x(\lambda) R_x(\mu).$$

□ **PROOF**
$$R_x(\lambda) = R_x(\lambda)(x - \mu 1) R_x(\mu)$$
$$= R_x(\lambda)(x - \lambda 1 + (\lambda - \mu)1) R_x(\mu)$$
$$= (1 + (\lambda - \mu) R_x(\lambda)) R_x(\mu)$$
$$= R_x(\mu) + (\lambda - \mu) R_x(\lambda) R_x(\mu).$$

THEOREM 6.4 The inverse mapping $x \mapsto x^{-1}$ from G onto G is continuous and hence a homeomorphism. In particular, $R_x: \rho(x) \to A$ is continuous for each $x \in A$.

□ **PROOF** Given $x_0 \in G$ and *any* $x \in G$ with $\|x - x_0\| < (2\|x_0^{-1}\|)^{-1}$, we have

$$\|x_0^{-1}x - 1\| = \|x_0^{-1}(x - x_0)\| \leq \|x_0^{-1}\| \|x - x_0\| < \tfrac{1}{2}. \tag{1}$$

Hence by Theorem 6.1, $x_0^{-1}x$ has inverse $x^{-1}x_0 = \sum_{i=0}^{\infty}(1 - x_0^{-1}x)^i$. Thus

$$\|x^{-1} - x_0^{-1}\| = \|(x^{-1}x_0 - 1)x_0^{-1}\| \leq \|x_0^{-1}\| \|x^{-1}x_0 - 1\|$$

$$= \|x_0^{-1}\| \left\| \sum_{i=1}^{\infty} (1 - x_0^{-1}x)^i \right\|$$

$$\leq \|x_0^{-1}\| \sum_{i=1}^{\infty} \|(1 - x_0^{-1}x)\|^i$$

$$= \frac{\|x_0^{-1}\| \|1 - x_0^{-1}x\|}{1 - \|1 - x_0^{-1}x\|} < 2\|x_0^{-1}\| \|1 - x_0^{-1}x\|$$

$$\leq 2\|x_0^{-1}\|^2 \|x - x_0\|,$$

where the strict inequality step follows from (1). This establishes the continuity of the inverse map. Finally, if $\lambda_n \to \lambda$, then $x - \lambda_n 1 \to x - \lambda 1$ and hence $R_x(\lambda_n) \to R_x(\lambda)$. Thus R_x is also continuous on its domain $\rho(x)$.

We are now prepared to prove a fundamental result which, with its subsequent corollary, will be crucial to what follows.

THEOREM 6.5 For every $x \in A$, $\sigma(x)$ is nonempty.

□ **PROOF** Given any $f \in A^*$ (the conjugate space of the Banach *space A*), define $g: \rho(x) \to \mathbf{C}$ by $g = f \circ R_x$. We now show that g is analytic on the open set $\rho(x)$. Applying f to both sides of the resolvent equation and using linearity properties, we obtain for $\lambda, \mu \in \rho(x)$:

$$\frac{g(\lambda) - g(\mu)}{\lambda - \mu} = f(R_x(\lambda)R_x(\mu)).$$

Since R_x is continuous, we then have

$$\lim_{\lambda \to \mu} \frac{g(\lambda) - g(\mu)}{\lambda - \mu} = f(R_x^2(\mu)).$$

Thus g is differentiable at each $\mu \in \rho(x)$ and hence analytic on $\rho(x)$. Now suppose $\sigma(x)$ were empty, so that $\rho(x) = \mathbf{C}$. Since

$$R_x(\lambda) = (x - \lambda 1)^{-1} = \lambda^{-1}(x/\lambda - 1)^{-1},$$

we note that $R_x(\lambda) \to 0$ as $\lambda \to \infty$ and that the same is true for $g(\lambda)$ since f is continuous. We would then have g analytic and bounded on all of $\rho(x) = \mathbf{C}$, which by Liouville's theorem would force $g = f \circ R_x$ to be a constant function (and in fact the 0 function). Since $f \in A^*$ was arbitrary, the fact that A^* is total (or separates points) yields the fact that $R_x = 0$, which is clearly impossible since $R_x(\lambda)$ is the inverse of $x - \lambda 1$ and thus cannot be 0. This contradicts the supposition that $\sigma(x) = \emptyset$ and completes the proof.

COROLLARY   Gelfand–Mazur Theorem

If a Banach algebra A is also a *division algebra* (every nonzero $x \in A$ has an inverse), then $A \cong \mathbf{C}$ under a natural algebra isomorphism.

□ **PROOF**   Given $x \in A$ we show that there exists $\lambda \in \mathbf{C}$ such that $x = \lambda 1$. Indeed if no such λ existed then $x - \lambda 1$ would never be 0. The division algebra property gives $\sigma(x) = \emptyset$, contradicting Theorem 6.5. Thus each $x \in A$ corresponds to a (necessarily unique) member of $\mathbf{C}$ and the correspondence is an isometric *algebra* isomorphism, preserving multiplicative as well as linear structure.

It should be noted that the nonemptiness of the spectrum and its corollary (with $\mathbf{C}$ replaced by $\mathbf{R}$) do not hold if we consider *real* Banach algebras, and this is one main reason for requiring complex Banach algebras (and complex Hilbert spaces in Chapter 5).

Specifically, consider the transformation $T: \mathbf{R}^2 \to \mathbf{R}^2$ which rotates the plane clockwise by 90°,

$$T \text{ `` = ''} \begin{bmatrix} 0 & -1 \\ 1 & 0 \end{bmatrix}.$$

Then $T - \lambda I$ is invertible on $\mathbf{R}^2$ for all $\lambda \in \mathbf{R}$. Also the quaternions provide an example of a real Banach division algebra that does not coincide with $\mathbf{R}$. There are natural connections between these comments and the fact that the fundamental theorem of algebra (every nonconstant polynomial in $\mathbf{C}$ has a root in $\mathbf{C}$) does not hold in $\mathbf{R}$. In fact the powerful Liouville theorem, which we used to show that $\sigma(x) \neq \emptyset$, is a commonly used means of proving the fundamental theorem of algebra.

Given $x \in A$ and a polynomial p with coefficients $\{\alpha_i\}_{i=0}^n$ in $\mathbf{C}$, we may regard $p(x) = \sum_{i=0}^n \alpha_i x^i$ as a member of A. Also if S is a subset of $\mathbf{C}$, we define

$$p(S) = \{\lambda \in \mathbf{C} : \lambda = p(s) \text{ for some } s \in S\}.$$

THEOREM 6.6   **Spectral Mapping Theorem**
$$\sigma(p(x)) = p(\sigma(x)).$$

□ **PROOF** $\sigma(p(x)) \subseteq p(\sigma(x))$: Given $\lambda \in \sigma(p(x))$, we then know that $p(x) - \lambda 1$ is not invertible. Factoring the polynomial $p(z) - \lambda$ in $\mathbf{C}$ we may write

$$p(z) - \lambda = \alpha \prod_{i=1}^n (z - \lambda_i),$$

with α and $\{\lambda_i\}_{i=1}^n$ in $\mathbf{C}$ and $\alpha \neq 0$. Hence for $x \in A$,

$$p(x) - \lambda 1 = \alpha \prod_{i=1}^n (x - \lambda_i 1).$$

Since $p(x) - \lambda 1$ is not invertible, there must exist at least one λ_i such that $x - \lambda_i 1$ is not invertible and hence $\lambda_i \in \sigma(x)$. Since $p(\lambda_i) - \lambda = 0$, we conclude that $\lambda \in p(\sigma(x))$. Thus $\sigma(p(x)) \subseteq p(\sigma(x))$.

$p(\sigma(x)) \subseteq \sigma(p(x))$: Let p be a polynomial with complex coefficients, let $\lambda \in \mathbf{C}$, and let z be an indeterminate. We may then write $p(z) - p(\lambda) = (z - \lambda)q(z)$, $q(z)$ a polynomial, since λ is a root of the polynomial $p(z) - p(\lambda)$. Given $\mu \in p(\sigma(x))$, we have $\mu = p(\lambda)$ with $\lambda \in \sigma(x)$. Letting $x \in A$ replace z above, we obtain

$$p(x) - p(\lambda)1 = (x - \lambda 1)q(x).$$

We may conclude that $p(\lambda) \in \sigma(p(x))$ since otherwise we would have an inverse for $x - \lambda 1$ (namely $R_{p(x)}(p(\lambda)) \cdot q(x)$), contradicting $\lambda \in \sigma(x)$. This shows that $p(\sigma(x)) \subseteq \sigma(p(x))$, completing the proof.

Given $x \in A$, we define the *spectral radius* $r(x)$ of x by

$$r(x) = \sup_{\lambda \in \sigma(x)} |\lambda|.$$

Note from the proof of Theorem 6.2 that $r(x) \leq \|x\|$.

THEOREM 6.7   For any $x \in A$, $r(x) = \lim_{n \to \infty} \|x^n\|^{1/n}$.

□ **PROOF**   Applying the spectral mapping theorem to $p(z) = z^n$, we obtain $r(x^n) = (r(x))^n$; and since $r(x^n) \leq \|x^n\|$, we have $(r(x))^n \leq \|x^n\|$ and hence $r(x) \leq \|x^n\|^{1/n}$ for all n. Working in the reverse direction, we will show that for *every* t with $r(x) < t$, $\|x^n\|^{1/n} \leq t$ for all but finitely many n. Given any $\lambda \in \mathbf{C}$ with $|\lambda| > \|x\|$, we have

$$R_x(\lambda) = (x - \lambda 1)^{-1} = -\lambda^{-1}(1 - x/\lambda)^{-1} = -\lambda^{-1} \sum_{n=0}^{\infty} (x/\lambda)^n.$$

Given *any* $f \in A^*$ and applying the above, we obtain with $g = f \circ R_x$,

$$g(\lambda) = f(R_x(\lambda)) = -\lambda^{-1} \sum_{n=0}^{\infty} f(x^n/\lambda^n) = -\lambda^{-1} \sum_{n=0}^{\infty} f(x^n)\lambda^{-n}.$$

We have already shown in Theorem 6.5 that g is analytic on all of $\rho(x)$, and complex variable theory enables us to conclude that the above *Laurent expansion* (in λ) for g can be extended to the region $\{\lambda \in \mathbf{C} : \lambda > r(x)\} \subseteq \rho(x)$ (see the analysis Preliminaries section). Choosing s such that $r(x) < s < t$ and letting $\lambda = s$ in the Laurent expansion, we conclude that $\sum_{n=0}^{\infty} f(x^n)s^{-n}$ converges and hence that its terms $\{f(x^n/s^n)\}$ form a bounded sequence. Since this is true for every $f \in A^*$, the corollary following the uniform boundedness principle (Theorem 3.12) enables us to conclude that $\{x^n/s^n\}$ is a bounded sequence in A; i.e., there exists $K > 0$ such that $\|x^n/s^n\| \leq K$ for all n. Thus we have $\|x^n\|^{1/n} \leq K^{1/n}s \leq t$ for all sufficiently large n ($K^{1/n} \to 1$ as $n \to \infty$). Overall we then have for any $\epsilon > 0$ and n large enough,

$$r(x) \le \| x^n \|^{1/n} \le r(x) + \epsilon,$$

which establishes the existence of $\lim \| x^n \|^{1/n}$ and its equality with $r(x)$.

□ THE MAXIMAL IDEAL SPACE

We now make the assumption that the Banach algebra A under consideration is commutative. Though some parts of the forthcoming development (but not certain crucial parts) can be obtained in the noncommutative case, we choose to make the simplifying commutativity assumption at this time.

An *ideal* I of a commutative Banach algebra A is a linear subspace of A such that $AI \subseteq I$, where

$$AI = \{ xi \in A : x \in A \quad \text{and} \quad i \in I \}.$$

Thus I is a ring ideal of A viewed as a commutative ring and a subspace of A viewed as a linear space.

A *maximal ideal* M of A is a proper ($M \ne A$) ideal that is properly contained in no other proper ideal.

EXERCISE 6.4   Let A be a commutative Banach algebra with identity.

a. Prove that no proper ideal in A can contain an invertible element.

b. Prove that every singular element x in A is contained in some maximal ideal. Hint: Show first that x belongs to the proper ideal $I = Ax$ and then use Zorn's lemma.

c. Prove that every maximal ideal M in A is closed in the topology on A. Hint: Show that if M is a proper ideal then $\overline{M}$ is also an ideal which is still a subset of the (closed) set S of singular elements.

THEOREM 6.8   Let A be a commutative Banach algebra with identity.

a. If I is a closed ideal in A, then A/I is a Banach algebra.
b. If M is a maximal ideal in A, then $A/M \cong \mathbf{C}$.

□ **PROOF**   (a) We have already shown in Theorem 3.1 that A/I is a Banach space with norm defined by $\|x + I\| = \inf_{i \in I} \|x + i\|$. We will not prove the standard result that A/I is an algebra with the (well-defined) multiplication $(x + I)(y + I) = xy + I$, and identity $1 + I$. Also,

$$\|(x + I)(y + I)\| = \|xy + I\| = \inf_{i \in I} \|xy + i\|$$
$$\leq \inf_{i_1, i_2 \in I} \|xy + xi_2 + yi_1 + i_1 i_2\|$$
$$= \inf_{i_1, i_2 \in I} \|(x + i_1)(y + i_2)\|$$
$$\leq \inf_{i_1, i_2 \in I} \|x + i_1\| \, \|y + i_2\|$$
$$= \|x + I\| \, \|y + I\|.$$

Finally, $\|1 + I\| = \inf_{i \in I} \|1 + i\| \leq 1$ and, on the other hand,

$$\|1 + I\| = \|(1 + I)^2\| \leq \|1 + I\|^2 \Longrightarrow \|1 + I\| \geq 1.$$

Thus we conclude that $\|1 + I\| = 1$.

(b) If M is a maximal ideal, then regarding A as a *commutative* ring, we accept the standard result that A/M is a field. Hence A/M is a division algebra. Applying the Gelfand–Mazur theorem, we conclude that $A/M \cong \mathbf{C}$. In what follows we always identify A/M and $\mathbf{C}$ by the *natural* isomorphism of that theorem. Note that commutativity is essential here since without it A/M need not even be a division ring.

We now consider the collection $\mathfrak{M}$ of all maximal ideals of A. Then $\mathfrak{M}$ is called the *maximal ideal space* for A. We topologize $\mathfrak{M}$ as follows. Given $x \in A$ define $\hat{x} \colon \mathfrak{M} \to \mathbf{C}$ by

$\hat{x}(M) =$ the complex number identified with $x + M \in A/M \cong \mathbf{C}$.

Give $\mathfrak{M}$ the *weak topology* generated by the collection $\hat{A} = \{\hat{x} : x \in A\}$. Thus a neighborhood subbase at $M_0 \in \mathfrak{M}$ consists of sets of the form

$$\mathcal{N}(M_0, \hat{x}, \epsilon) = \{M \in \mathfrak{M} : |\hat{x}(M) - \hat{x}(M_0)| < \epsilon\}$$
$$(\hat{x} \in \hat{A} \text{ and } \epsilon > 0).$$

In order to obtain more information about this topological space $\mathfrak{M}$, we now show that it is homeomorphic with a subset of a somewhat more familiar space. We define the set Δ of *nonzero continuous multiplicative linear functionals* (algebra homomorphisms) on A. Thus

$$\Delta = \{f \in A^* : f \neq 0 \text{ and } f(xy) = f(x)f(y) \text{ for all } x, y \in A\}.$$

Since $\Delta \subseteq A^*$, the conjugate space of the Banach space A, we can endow Δ with its relative weak* topology as a subspace of A^*. Thus a typical subbasic open neighborhood of $f_0 \in \Delta$ is defined by

$$U(f_0, \hat{x}, \epsilon) = \{f \in \Delta : |\hat{x}(f) - \hat{x}(f_0)| < \epsilon\},$$

$$(\hat{x} \in \hat{A} \quad \text{and} \quad \epsilon > 0),$$

where $\hat{x}(f) = f(x)$. Note that the same collection $\hat{A}$ generates the topologies on $\mathfrak{M}$ and on Δ.

In order to illustrate the concepts of maximal ideal space $\mathfrak{M}$ and the closely related space Δ we digress briefly from our general development to consider these spaces in the special case where $A = \mathcal{C}(S)$, S compact and Hausdorff. For each point p in S, define

$$M_p = \{f \in \mathcal{C}(S) : f(p) = 0\}$$

and note the $M_p = \ker(h_p)$ where $h_p \in \Delta$ is defined by $h_p(f) = f(p)$. We will show that the subsets M_p, $p \in S$, are precisely the maximal ideals of $\mathcal{C}(S)$, establishing a one-to-one correspondence between members of $\mathfrak{M}$ and points of S (and also between $\mathfrak{M}$ and Δ). Note that $p \neq q$ implies $M_p \neq M_q$ since Urysohn's lemma (S compact Hausdorff implies S normal) can be applied to obtain $f \in \mathcal{C}(S)$ with $f(p) = 0$ and $f(q) \neq 0$. It is readily checked that each M_p is a proper ideal, and maximality results from Lemma 6.9b following since $M_p = \ker(h_p)$ and $h_p \in \Delta$. To see that every $M \in \mathfrak{M}$ is an M_p for some $p \in S$ suppose, on the contrary, that for each $p \in S$ there exists some $f_p \in M$ such that $f_p(p) \neq 0$. Since S is compact, we can find $\{f_{p_i}\}_{i=1}^n$ such that $f = \sum_{i=1}^n f_{p_i} f_{p_i}^*$ is nowhere zero on S. But then f is an invertible element of the maximal ideal M which is impossible by Exercise 6.4a. Thus we see in this case that $\mathfrak{M}$ (or Δ) can be naturally identified with S, providing an algebraic way of viewing the points of S. This will, we hope, offer important motivation for the following sections, where an abstract commutative Banach algebra A (where there is no underlying set of points) will be related to $\mathcal{C}(\mathfrak{M})$, $\mathfrak{M}$ being the maximal ideal space of A.

We now return to the general case of a commutative Banach algebra A with identity.

LEMMA 6.9
    a. $f, g \in \Delta$ and $\ker(f) = \ker(g) = M \Rightarrow f = g$.
    b. Given $f \in \Delta$ and $M = \ker(f)$, then M is a maximal ideal in A; the quotient map $f_M : A \to A/M \cong \mathbf{C}$ coincides with f; and $\hat{x}(M) = \hat{x}(f)$ for all $x \in A$.
    c. Δ and $\mathfrak{M}$ are homeomorphic.
    d. $\mathfrak{M}$ is a compact Hausdorff space.

□   **PROOF**   (a) Since $\ker(f) = \ker(g)$, Lemma 2.4c shows that $g = \alpha f$. Since f and g are nonzero and multiplicative, $f(1) = g(1) = 1$. It then follows that $\alpha = 1$ and hence $f = g$.

(b) It is readily seen that M is a proper ideal in A, and maximality results as follows. If $x_0 \notin M$ then by Lemma 2.4b, $\text{span}(M \cup \{x_0\}) = A$; so it is not possible to enlarge M to a *proper* ideal. Thus M is maximal and $A/M \cong \mathbf{C}$ by Theorem 6.8b. Since the quotient map $f_M : A \to A/M \cong \mathbf{C}$ defined by $f_M(x) = x + M$ is (upon identifying $x + M$ with its counterpart in $\mathbf{C}$) in Δ, we conclude by (a) that $f = f_M$ since f and f_M both have M as kernel. Finally, $\hat{x}(M)$ and $\hat{x}(f)$ are both the complex number identified with $x + M$.

(c) The mapping $h : \Delta \to \mathfrak{M}$ defined by $h(f) = \ker(f)$ is well defined and injective by (a) and (b). It is surjective by (b) since for each $M \in \mathfrak{M}$, $f_M \in \Delta$. Finally, h is a homeomorphism by virtue of the identical nature of the $\hat{A}$ induced topologies on Δ and $\mathfrak{M}$. In fact each subbasic open neighborhood $U(f_{M_0}, \hat{x}, \epsilon)$ in Δ maps under h to the corresponding neighborhood $\mathcal{N}(M_0, \hat{x}, \epsilon)$ in $\mathfrak{M}$. Thus the topologies coincide.

(d) We will show that Δ is a compact Hausdorff space, in which case (c) ensures the same is true for M. Since $f \in \Delta$ coincides with a quotient map f_M where $M = \ker(f) \in \mathfrak{M}$, we have

$$\| f_M(x) \| = \| x + M \| = \inf_{m \in M} \| x + m \| \le \| x \|$$

and hence $\| f \| = \| f_M \| \le 1$. On the other hand, since $| f(1) | = | 1 | = 1$, we have $\| f \| = 1$ for all $f \in \Delta$. Hence Δ is a subset of the closed unit ball S^* in A^* and the topology on Δ coincides with its inherited relative topology as a subset of S^* with the weak* topology (both topologies are generated by $\hat{A}$). By the Banach–Alaoglu theorem S^* is compact in the weak* topology, and S^* is Hausdorff in this topology since A^* is ($\hat{A}$ separates points). It then suffices to show that Δ is closed in S^*. Since the 0 functional is not in the closure of Δ ($\hat{1}(0) = 0$, but $\hat{1}(f) = f(1) = 1$ for all $f \in \Delta$) it is enough to show that $\Delta \cup \{0\}$ is closed in S^*. Accordingly,

$$\Delta \cup \{0\} = \bigcap_{x,y \in A} \{f \in S^* : f(xy) - f(x)f(y) = 0\}$$
$$= \bigcap_{x,y \in A} \{f \in S^* : f \in \ker(\widehat{xy} - \hat{x}\hat{y})\},$$

so $\Delta \cup \{0\}$ is closed in S^* as the intersection of closed sets. Thus Δ and its homeomorphic image $\mathfrak{M}$ are compact Hausdorff spaces.

□   **GELFAND REPRESENTATION THEORY**

For what follows, we need two more algebraic concepts specialized to a commutative Banach algebra A. The *radical R* of A is defined to be the intersection of all its maximal ideals. The algebra A is said to be *semisimple* if $R = \{0\}$.

We are now prepared to present a fundamental result of the commutative theory. Our goal is to *represent* an arbitrary commutative Banach algebra A with identity as a subspace of a function algebra $\mathfrak{C}(X)$, X a compact Hausdorff space, by means of a natural structure preserving mapping. We denote by $\mathfrak{C}(\mathfrak{M})$ the set of all continuous, complex-valued functions on the compact Hausdorff space $\mathfrak{M}$ of maximal ideals of A. Note that $\hat{A}$ is a subspace of $\mathfrak{C}(\mathfrak{M})$, so that both spaces can be naturally endowed with the sup norm, which we denote by $\| \ \|_\infty$ ($\| f \|_\infty = \sup_{M \in \mathfrak{M}} | f(M) |$).

THEOREM 6.10   Gelfand Representation Theorem
The *Gelfand mapping*

$$\wedge : x \mapsto \hat{x}$$

is a continuous algebra homomorphism from the commutative Banach algebra A *into* the Banach algebra $\mathfrak{C}(\mathfrak{M})$, and $\wedge : A \rightarrow$

$\mathcal{C}(\mathfrak{M})$ satisfies the following properties:

a. $\|\hat{x}\|_\infty \leq \|x\|$ (which forces $\wedge$ to be continuous).

b. A is a subalgebra of $\mathcal{C}(\mathfrak{M})$ and $\hat{A}$ separates points in M:

$$M_1, M_2 \in \mathfrak{M} \quad \text{and} \quad M_1 \neq M_2$$

$$\Rightarrow \hat{x}(M_1) \neq \hat{x}(M_2) \quad \text{for some} \quad \hat{x} \in \hat{A}.$$

c. If R is the radical of A, then

$$R = \{x \in A : \hat{x} = 0\},$$

so that $\wedge$ is injective if and only if A is semisimple.

d. $x \in A$ is invertible $\Longleftrightarrow x \notin M$ for every $M \in \mathfrak{M}$
$\Longleftrightarrow x(M) \neq 0$ for every $M \in \mathfrak{M}$.

e. For every $x \in A$, $\sigma(x) = \text{range}(\hat{x})$ and $r(x) = \|\hat{x}\|_\infty$.

□ **PROOF** Since the topology on $\mathfrak{M}$ is the weakest such that every $\hat{x} \in \hat{A}$ is continuous on $\mathfrak{M}$, it is clear that $\hat{A} \subset \mathcal{C}(\mathfrak{M})$ and hence that $\wedge$ maps A into $\mathcal{C}(\mathfrak{M})$. The fact that $\wedge$ is an algebra homomorphism follows from

$$\widehat{xy}(M) = \text{the complex number identified with } xy + M$$
$$= f_M(xy) = f_M(x)f_M(y)$$
$$= \hat{x}(M)\hat{y}(M).$$

Additivity and homogeneity follow similarly. Continuity of $\wedge$ follows from (a) below.

(a)

$$\|\hat{x}\|_\infty = \sup_{M \in \mathfrak{M}} |\hat{x}(M)| = \sup_{M \in \mathfrak{M}} |f_M(x)| \leq \|x\|,$$

where the inequality follows since $\|f_M\| = 1$ for all $M \in \mathfrak{M}$ as shown in the proof of Lemma 6.9d. This establishes the continuity of $\wedge$ since

$$x_n \to 0 \Longrightarrow \|x_n\| \to 0 \Longrightarrow \|\hat{x}_n\|_\infty \to 0 \Longrightarrow \hat{x}_n \to 0,$$

and continuity at 0 implies continuity on all of A.

(b) Clearly A is a (not necessarily closed) subalgebra of $\mathcal{C}(\mathfrak{M})$. Given $M_1, M_2 \in \mathfrak{M}$ with $M_1 \neq M_2$, then $f_{M_1} \neq f_{M_2}$ where $f_{M_i} : A \to A/M_i \cong \mathbf{C}$ ($i = 1,2$) is the natural quotient map. Hence there exists $x \in A$ such that $f_{M_1}(x) \neq f_{M_2}(x)$ from which it follows that $\hat{x}(M_1) \neq \hat{x}(M_2)$. Thus $\hat{A}$ separates points in $\mathfrak{M}$.

(c)

$$x \in R \Longleftrightarrow x \in M \qquad \text{for all} \quad M \in \mathfrak{M}$$
$$\Longleftrightarrow f_M(x) = \hat{x}(M) = 0 \quad \text{for all} \qquad M \in \mathfrak{M}$$
$$\Longleftrightarrow \hat{x} = 0,$$

so $R = \{x \in A : \hat{x} = 0\}$. Thus we have

$$\wedge \text{ injective} \Longleftrightarrow x = 0 \quad \text{whenever} \quad \hat{x} = 0$$
$$\Longleftrightarrow x = 0 \quad \text{whenever} \quad x \in R$$
$$\Longleftrightarrow R = \{0\}.$$

(d)

$$x \in A \text{ invertible} \Longrightarrow x \notin M \quad \text{for every} \quad M \in \mathfrak{M}$$
$$\text{(Exercise 6.4a)}$$
$$\Longleftrightarrow x(M) \neq 0 \quad \text{for every} \quad M \in \mathfrak{M}$$
$$\text{(since } \hat{x}(M) = f_M(x)\text{)}.$$

Conversely,

$$x \text{ singular} \Longrightarrow x \in I \quad \text{where} \quad I = Ax \quad \text{is proper} \quad (1 \notin I)$$
$$\Longrightarrow x \in M \quad \text{for some} \quad M \in \mathfrak{M} \text{ with } M \supseteq I$$
$$\text{(Exercise 6.4b)}.$$

(e)

$$\lambda \in \sigma(x) \Longleftrightarrow x - \lambda 1 \quad \text{singular} \Longleftrightarrow \widehat{x - \lambda 1}(M) = 0$$
$$\text{for some} \quad M \in \mathfrak{M}$$
$$\Longleftrightarrow \hat{x}(M) = \lambda,$$

so $\sigma(x) = \text{range}(\hat{x})$. Finally,

$$r(x) = \sup_{\lambda \in \sigma(x)} |\lambda| = \sup_{M \in \mathfrak{M}} |\hat{x}(M)| = \|x\|_\infty.$$

We now consider conditions under which the Gelfand mapping provides an even stronger relation between A and $\mathcal{C}(\mathfrak{M})$, our ultimate goal being the case where $\wedge$ is an isometric isomorphism of A onto $\mathcal{C}(\mathfrak{M})$. As a first step we have

LEMMA 6.11 Let A be a commutative Banach algebra (with identity). Then the following are equivalent:

(a) $\|x^2\| = \|x\|^2$ for all $x \in A$.
(b) $r(x) = \|x\|$ for all $x \in A$.
(c) $\|\hat{x}\|_\infty = \|x\|$ for all $x \in A$.

□ **PROOF**   (a) $\Rightarrow$ (b): From (a) we obtain for all $k = 1, 2, \ldots,$

$$\|x^{2^k}\| = \|x^{2^{k-1}}\|^2 = \cdots = \|x\|^{2^k}.$$

Hence we have

$$r(x) = \lim_{n \to \infty} \|x^n\|^{1/n} = \lim_{k \to \infty} \|x^{2^k}\|^{2^{-k}} = \lim_{k \to \infty} \|x\| = \|x\|.$$

(b) $\Rightarrow$ (a): For any $x \in A$ we have

$$\|x\| = r(x) \Rightarrow \|x^2\| = r(x^2) = (r(x))^2 = \|x\|^2,$$

where $r(x^2) = (r(x))^2$ by the spectral mapping Theorem (6.6) with $p(x) = x^2$.

(b) $\Leftrightarrow$ (c): This follows directly from Theorem 6.10e.

EXERCISE 6.5   Let A be a commutative Banach algebra satisfying condition (c) of Lemma 6.11. Prove that the Gelfand mapping $\wedge$ is an isometric, injective algebra homomorphism of A into $\mathfrak{C}(\mathfrak{M})$ and that $\hat{A}$ is a *closed* subspace of $\mathfrak{C}(\mathfrak{M})$.

□ **B* ALGEBRAS**

We now consider some special Banach algebras whose elements, in the commutative case, satisfy one (and hence all) of the conditions of the above lemma. A (not necessarily commutative) Banach algebra A is called a *B* algebra* if there exists a unary operation $(x \mapsto x^*)$ on A satisfying for all $x, y \in A$, $\alpha \in \mathbf{C}$:

(a) $(x + y)^* = x^* + y^*$.
(b) $(\alpha x)^* = \alpha^* x^*$.
(c) $(xy)^* = y^* x^*$.
(d) $x^{**} = x$.
(e) $\|x^* x\| = \|x\|^2$.
Properties (a)–(d) make $*$ an *involution* on A.

Two examples of B^* algebras which will interest us are

1. $\mathcal{C}(\mathcal{S})$ or a closed subalgebra that contains the complex conjugate function $(f^*(s) = (f(s))^*)$ of each of its members. Thus the involution in this case maps a function f onto a function f^*, and it is readily seen that $*$ satisfies all the required properties for a B^* algebra.

2. $\mathcal{B}(H)$ or a closed subalgebra that is closed under the adjoint operation. Here the involution maps $T \in \mathcal{B}(H)$ into $T^* \in \mathcal{B}(H)$. The fact that a B^* algebra results is a consequence of Theorem 5.11.

Many of the special kinds of operators in $\mathcal{B}(H)$ have direct generalizations in a B^* algebra setting. Thus if A is a B^* algebra we say $x \in A$ is *self-adjoint* if $x = x^*$, *normal* if $xx^* = x^*x$, and a *projection* if $x^2 = x$.

EXERCISE 6.6 Let A be a B^* algebra with $x, y \in A$.

    a. Prove that x, y, and xy self-adjoint $\Longrightarrow x$ and y commute.
    b. Prove that x normal $\Longrightarrow \|x^*\| = \|x\|$.
    c. Prove that x a nonzero projection $\Longrightarrow \|x\| \geq 1$.

LEMMA 6.12 If x is normal in a B^* algebra, then $\|x^2\| = \|x\|^2$.

□ **PROOF** Applying property (e) of B^* algebras to x, to x^*x, and to x^2, we obtain

$$\|x\|^4 = \|x^*x\|^2 = \|(x^*x)^*(x^*x)\|$$
$$= \|x^*xx^*x\| = \|(x^*)^2x^2\| = \|(x^2)^*x^2\|$$
$$= \|x^2\|^2.$$

Taking square roots completes the proof.

□ **APPROXIMATION AND
THE GELFAND–NEUMARK THEOREM**

We now state without proof two important approximation theorems, the second of which is a generalization of the first. (See Simmons' book [1, Chapter 7] for developments and proofs.)

THEOREM 6.13   **Weierstrass Approximation Theorem**
Given a compact subset K of **R**, the polynomials on K are dense in $\mathcal{C}(K)$, where all functions on K are *real*-valued and the sup norm is used.

THEOREM 6.14   **Complex Stone–Weierstrass Theorem**
Let S be a compact Hausdorff space and A a subalgebra of $\mathcal{C}(S)$ (complex-valued functions) such that A separates points of S, contains a nonzero constant function, and is closed under conjugation ($f \in A \Rightarrow f^* \in A$). Then A is dense in $\mathcal{C}(S)$.

The following important theorem characterizes B^* algebras in a most pleasing way.

THEOREM 6.15   **Gelfand–Neumark Theorem**
If A is a commutative B^* algebra then $\wedge : A \to \mathcal{C}(\mathfrak{M})$ is a *-preserving isometric isomorphism.

□   **PROOF**   Every $x \in A$ is normal since A is commutative. Thus by Lemmas 6.12, 6.11, and Exercise 6.5 we need only prove that $\wedge$ is surjective and that $\widehat{x^*} = (\hat{x})^*$ for all $x \in A$. We deal with the latter problem first. If we first assume that x is self-adjoint, this reduces to showing that $\hat{x}$ is real-valued (i.e., $\hat{x} = (\hat{x})^*$). Suppose, on the contrary, that $\hat{x}(M) = \alpha + i\beta$, $\beta \neq 0$, for some $M \in \mathfrak{M}$. Then $y = (x - \alpha 1)/\beta \in A$ is also self-adjoint and $\hat{y}(M) = i$, from which it follows that $y - i1 \in M$. Since $M^* = \{m^* : m \in M\} \in \mathfrak{M}$ and since $y + i1 \in M^*$, we have $\hat{y}(M^*) = -i$. Given any $t > 0$,

$$\widehat{(y - it1)}(M^*) = -i(1 + t) \quad \text{and} \quad \widehat{(y + it1)} \cdot (M) = i(1 + t).$$

Hence $1 + t \leq \|y - it1\|_\infty$ and $1 + t \leq \|y + it1\|_\infty$. Multiplying these inequalities, we obtain

$$\begin{aligned}
(1 + t)^2 &\leq \|y - it1\| \, \|y + it1\| = \|(y + it1)^*\| \, \|y + it1\| \\
&= \|(y + it1)^*(y + it1)\| \\
&= \|(y - it1)(y + it1)\| = \|y^2 + t^2 1\| \\
&\leq \|y^2\| + t^2.
\end{aligned}$$

This results in the inequality $1 + 2t \leq \|y^2\|$ which, since $t > 0$ was arbitrary, establishes a contradiction and ensures that x

self-adjoint implies $\widehat{x^*} = (\hat{x})$.* Now given any (necessarily normal) $x \in A$, we may write $x = y + iz$ where $y = (x + x^*)/2$ and $z = (x - x^*)/2i$ are self-adjoint. Hence

$$\widehat{x^*}(M) = (\widehat{y - iz})(M) = \hat{y}(M) - i\hat{z}(M)$$
$$= (\hat{y}(M) + i\hat{z}(M))^* = (\hat{x}(M))^* = (\hat{x})^*(M),$$

so $\widehat{x^*} = (\hat{x})^*$. Thus $\wedge$ is *-preserving and $\hat{A}$ is closed under conjugation. Finally, $\hat{1}$ is a nonzero constant function in $\hat{A}$, and $\hat{A}$ separates points of $\mathfrak{M}$ by Theorem 6.10b. We conclude from the complex Stone–Weierstrass theorem that $\hat{A}$ is dense in $\mathfrak{C}(\mathfrak{M})$. Since $\hat{A}$ is closed, we have shown that $\hat{A} = \mathfrak{C}(\mathfrak{M})$, completing the proof.

EXERCISE 6.7   a. Use Theorem 6.15 to prove that if A is a commutative B^* algebra and $x \in A$ is self-adjoint, then $\hat{x} \in \mathfrak{C}(\mathfrak{M})$ is real and hence $\sigma(x) \subseteq \mathbf{R}$.

b. Prove that if T is a self-adjoint operator on a Hilbert space H, then $\sigma(T) \subseteq \mathbf{R}$ (cf. Problem 5.4). Hint: Let A be the closed subalgebra of $\mathfrak{B}(H)$ generated by T and show that $\sigma(T) \subseteq \sigma_A(T)$ (where $\sigma_A(T)$ is the spectrum of T viewed in the subalgebra A).

c. Use Theorem 5.14 to conclude that the spectrum of a positive operator on H is a subset of the nonnegative reals.

□ SPECTRAL THEOREM FOR BOUNDED NORMAL OPERATORS

We now develop one version of the spectral theorem. Let N be a normal operator in $\mathfrak{B}(H)$ and let A be the commutative B^* algebra generated by N and N^*. Thus A is the smallest closed subalgebra of $\mathfrak{B}(H)$ containing N and N^*, and familiar closure arguments show that A is indeed commutative and closed under adjoints. The Gelfand–Neumark theorem immediately shows that A is isometrically *-isomorphic (i.e., the isomorphism is *-preserving) to $\mathfrak{C}(\mathfrak{M})$, where $\mathfrak{M}$ is the maximal ideal space for A. We now wish to show that $\mathfrak{M}$ is homeomorphic with a much more familiar compact Hausdorff space, namely the set of complex numbers that comprise the spectrum of the operator N. This will shed some new light on the nature of normal and self-adjoint operators.

LEMMA 6.16　Let S be a compact Hausdorff space and let $\tilde{A}$ be a Banach subalgebra of $\mathfrak{C}(S)$. If $f \in \tilde{A}$ is a real-valued function that is invertible in $\mathfrak{C}(S)$, then f is invertible in $\tilde{A}$ (i.e., $f^{-1} \in \tilde{A}$).

□ **PROOF**　Since f is invertible and real-valued in $\mathfrak{C}(S)$, range (f) is a compact subset K of $\mathbf{R}$ not including 0. Given $\epsilon > 0$, the Weierstrass approximation theorem yields a polynomial p on K such that $|p(t) - 1/t| < \epsilon$ for all $t \in K$ (the reciprocal function is a uniform limit of polynomials). Hence $|p(f(s)) - 1/f(s)| < \epsilon$ for all $s \in S$, so that $\|p(f) - 1/f\| < \epsilon$. Since $\tilde{A}$ is an algebra and $f \in \tilde{A}$, $p(f) \in \tilde{A}$. Since $\epsilon > 0$ was arbitrary and $\tilde{A}$ is closed, $1/f = f^{-1} \in \tilde{A}$.

Let A denote the (commutative) B^* subalgebra of $\mathfrak{B}(H)$ generated by a normal operator N. The final auxiliary result which we need is that if T belongs to A, then $\sigma(T) = \sigma_A(T)$, where $\sigma_A(T)$ denotes the spectrum of T regarded as a member of A. Thus

$$\sigma_A(T) = \{\lambda \in \mathbf{C} : (T - \lambda I)^{-1} \text{ exists and } (T - \lambda I)^{-1} \in A\}$$

The equality of $\sigma(T)$ and $\sigma_A(T)$ will follow directly from:

LEMMA 6.17　Let A be a commutative B^* subalgebra of $\mathfrak{B}(H)$. Then $T \in A$ is invertible in $\mathfrak{B}(H) \Longleftrightarrow T$ is invertible in A.

□ **PROOF**　$\Longleftarrow$: T invertible in A $\Longrightarrow T^{-1} \in A \Longrightarrow T^{-1} \in \mathfrak{B}(H)$.
$\Longrightarrow$: Given T invertible in $\mathfrak{B}(H)$ and $T \in A$, assume first that T is self-adjoint. Then T^{-1} is seen (using Theorem 5.12) to be self-adjoint since

$$\langle T^{-1}x, x \rangle = \langle T^{-1}x, T(T^{-1}x) \rangle \in \mathbf{R}.$$

Let B be the commutative B^* algebra generated by T and T^{-1}. Then B is isometrically isomorphic to $\mathfrak{C}(\mathfrak{M}_B)$, where $\mathfrak{M}_B$ is the maximal ideal space of B. Also $\hat{T} \in \mathfrak{C}(\mathfrak{M}_B)$ is a real-valued function on $\mathfrak{M}_B$, and $C = A \cap B$ is a Banach subalgebra of B and hence is isometrically isomorphic to a Banach subalgebra of $\mathfrak{C}(\mathfrak{M}_B)$. Since $T \in C$, Lemma 6.16 shows that $T^{-1} \in C$ and hence $T^{-1} \in A$. Now given a not necessarily self-adjoint T, invertible in $\mathcal{B}(H)$, then $U = TT^*$ is self-adjoint with inverse

$$U^{-1} = (T^*)^{-1}T^{-1} = (T^{-1})^*T^{-1}.$$

By what was done above, $U^{-1} \in A$; and by the commutativity of A we have $T(T^*U^{-1}) = T^*U^{-1}T = I$. We conclude that T has an inverse, namely T^*U^{-1}, which is a member of A since both T^* and U^{-1} are.

THEOREM 6.18   **Spectral Theorem for Bounded Normal Operators**
Given $N \in \mathcal{B}(H)$, N normal, and A the B^* algebra generated by N, then A is isometrically *-isomorphic to $\mathcal{C}(\sigma(N))$, and the image of N under the isomorphism is the identity function on $\sigma(N)$.

□   **PROOF**   In view of the Gelfand–Neumark theorem the main task of the proof is to show that the maximal ideal space $\mathfrak{M}$ of A is homeomorphic to $\sigma(N)$. By Theorem 6.10e and Lemma 6.17, $\sigma(N) = \sigma_A(N) = \text{range}(\hat{N})$. Furthermore $\hat{N}; \mathfrak{M} \rightarrow \sigma(N)$ is injective (and thus bijective) since

$$\hat{N}(M_1) = \hat{N}(M_2) \Rightarrow \widehat{N^*}(M_1) = (\hat{N}(M_1))^*$$
$$= (\hat{N}(M_2))^* = \widehat{N^*}(M_2)$$
$$\Rightarrow \hat{T}(M_1) = \hat{T}(M_2) \quad \text{for all}$$
$$\hat{T} \in \hat{A} = \mathcal{C}(\mathfrak{M}).$$

Since (Theorem 6.10b) $\mathcal{C}(\mathfrak{M})$ separates points in $\mathfrak{M}$ it follows that $M_1 = M_2$ and $\hat{N}$ is injective. Finally, since $\hat{N}$ is continuous, $\hat{N}$ will be a homeomorphism if $\hat{N}$ can be shown to be a closed mapping. But using the fact that $\mathfrak{M}$ and $\sigma(N)$ are compact and Hausdorff, K closed in $\mathfrak{M} \Rightarrow K$ compact in $\mathfrak{M} \Rightarrow \hat{N}(K)$ compact and hence closed in $\sigma(N)$. The fact that N is identified with the identity mapping on $\sigma(N)$ follows since $\hat{N}$ provides the homeomorphic identification between $\mathfrak{M}$ and $\sigma(N)$.

We can now use this spectral theorem to establish a number of nontrivial facts about normal (and hence self-adjoint, positive, and unitary) operators on a Hilbert space H. This is illustrated by the theorem and exercise following and also by Problem 4 in this chapter.

THEOREM 6.19 Every positive operator $T \in \mathcal{B}(H)$ has a self-adjoint square root $S \in \mathcal{B}(H)$ (i.e., $S^2 = T$).

☐ **PROOF** Applying the spectral theorem to the B^* algebra generated by T, we conclude that the image $\hat{T}$ of T under the isometric *-isomorphism can be viewed as the identity function on $\sigma(T)$. By Exercise 6.7c, $\sigma(T) \subseteq [0, \infty)$, so that $\hat{T}$ is nonnegative and continuous on $\sigma(T)$. Let $S \in \mathcal{B}(H)$ be the preimage of the nonnegative square root $\hat{S} \in \mathcal{C}(\sigma(T))$ of T. Then S is self-adjoint since $\hat{S} = (\hat{S})^*$, and it is easily seen that $S^2 = T$. (Problem 4 in this chapter shows that S is in fact positive.)

EXERCISE 6.8 Let U be a unitary operator on H. Prove that

$$\sigma(U) \subseteq \{\lambda \in \mathbf{C} : |\lambda| = 1\}.$$

In the Remarks at the end of this chapter a few of the many versions and generalizations of the spectral theorem are presented. Here we observe that we have generalized the finite-dimensional spectral theorem, which states that every normal operator (or matrix) on $\mathbf{C}^n$ can be written as a linear combination of orthogonal projections with mutually disjoint ranges; i.e., with $\sigma(N) = \{\lambda_i\}_{i=1}^m$ we have

$$N = \sum_{i=1}^m \lambda_i P_i \quad \text{where} \quad P_i P_j = \delta_{ij} P_i \quad \text{and} \quad \sum_{i=1}^m P_i = I.$$

This finite-dimensional result is an easy consequence of our spectral theorem since $\sigma(T)$ is a discrete space and hence all functions on $\sigma(T)$ are continuous. The projections arise by defining $\hat{P}_j$ on $\{\lambda_i\}_{i=1}^m$ by $P_j(\lambda_i) = \delta_{ij}$ and it is then quite immediate that

$$\hat{N} = \sum_{i=1}^m \lambda_i \hat{P}_i, \qquad \hat{P}_i \hat{P}_j = \delta_{ij} \hat{P}_i, \qquad \text{and} \qquad \sum_{i=1}^m \hat{P}_i = 1_{\sigma(N)}$$

($1_{\sigma(N)}$ is the multiplicative identity in $\mathcal{C}(\sigma(N))$.) An application of the inverse isometric *-isomorphism (i.e., $\wedge^{-1}$) establishes the result.

A commonly stated version of the above result is that a normal operator N decomposes its (finite-dimensional) domain into a direct sum of mutually orthogonal subspaces $\{M_i\}_{i=1}^m$ on each of which $\mathcal{N}$ is *invariant*, i.e., $\mathcal{N}(M_i) \subseteq M_i$. This follows from the above by choosing $M_i = \text{range}(P_i)$ and reduces the study of $\mathcal{N}$ on its domain to a study of presumably simpler operators $(\mathcal{N}|_{M_i})$ acting on simpler domains. The infinite-dimensional generalization of this decomposition (another version of the spectral theorem) is a valuable tool for studying normal operators and would obviously be of great value if extended in some form to general operators. It seems fitting to close by noting that we have motivated a (and perhaps the) fundamental unsolved problem of functional analysis:

Invariant Subspace Conjecture

Every (not necessarily normal) bounded operator on an infinite-dimensional separable Hilbert space has a nontrivial invariant subspace.

□   REMARKS

Our approach here has essentially been to develop as direct a route as possible to a Banach algebra proof of the spectral theorem. A general treatment of the rich and vital theory of Banach algebras can be found in Rickart's book [19]. It should also be pointed out that Banach algebras are playing a crucial role in theoretical formulations of quantum mechanics at a very much more sophisticated level than that of our brief mention in Chapter 5.

There are stronger and more versatile versions of the spectral theorem for both bounded and unbounded operators. We state two such results for bounded operators:

1. Given $T \in \mathcal{B}(H)$ with $T = T^*$, then associated with T is a *projection-valued (spectral) measure* E from the *Borel sets* of $\sigma(T)$ to the self-adjoint projection operators satisfying

$$T = \int_{\sigma(T)} f \, dE,$$

where f is the identity function on $\sigma(T)$.

2. Given $T \in \mathcal{B}(H)$ with T normal, then H is unitarily equiva-

lent to an L^2 space and under the equivalence T corresponds to a multiplication operator (by the identity function) on L^2.

Note that (1) provides a natural generalization of the finite-dimensional version involving orthogonal projections mentioned in the last section (sums are replaced by *spectral integrals*). For a development of the italicized concepts and the general result see Reed and Simon's book [20]. It turns out that the integral extension process of Chapter 4 can be used to extend the range (and of course the domain) of the isometric *-isomorphism of Gelfand–Neumark from $\mathbb{C}(\sigma(T))$ to $L^\infty(\sigma(T))$. This generates the desired projection operators (from characteristic functions of Borel sets).

A development of version (2) is nicely sketched in the expository article by Halmos [21], and this result adds considerable meaning to the content of Exercise 5.9.

Problem 5 considers the algebra of absolutely convergent Fourier series, which can be viewed as functions $f : [0, 2\pi) \to \mathbf{C}$ defined by

$$f(\theta) = \sum_{n=-\infty}^{\infty} \alpha_n e^{in\theta} \qquad \text{with} \qquad \sum_{n=-\infty}^{\infty} |\alpha_n| < \infty.$$

Problem 6 outlines Weiner's proof that a function defined by an absolutely convergent Fourier series which is nowhere zero has an inverse which also arises from an absolutely convergent Fourier series. This provides a strong example of the economy and elegance that functional analysis can bring to bear on a result with a rather laborious classical proof, and illustrates the claim made in the second sentence of the introduction in Chapter 1.

□ **PROBLEMS**

1. Let A be a Banach algebra without identity—so axiom (e) of the definition is not relevant. Let $\tilde{A} = A \times \mathbf{C}$ and define operations on $\tilde{A}$ as follows: Vector space operations are componentwise and

$$(x_1, \alpha_1) \cdot (x_2, \alpha_2) = (x_1 x_2 + \alpha_1 x_2 + \alpha_2 x_1, \alpha_1 \alpha_2).$$

Finally define $\| (x, \alpha) \| = \| x \| + | \alpha |$. Prove that $\tilde{A}$ is a Banach algebra with identity and that there is a natural isometric isomorphism of A onto a closed subalgebra of $\tilde{A}$.

2. Let A be any function algebra with identity. Thus A is an algebra of complex-valued functions on a set S with operations defined pointwise.

  a. Prove that if A contains an unbounded function f, then A cannot by any choice of norm be made into a Banach algebra. Hint: Argue that $\sigma(f) \supseteq \text{range}(f)$ and obtain a contradiction to a fundamental result of Banach algebra theory.

  b. Prove that $\mathcal{C}(D)$, the analytic functions on the open unit disk D, cannot be made into a Banach algebra.

3. Let T be an operator on a Hilbert space H and let

$$r(T) = \sup_{\lambda \in \sigma(T)} |\lambda|$$

be the spectral radius of T.

  a. Prove that if T is normal, then $r(T) = \|T\|$.

  b. Show that this result emphatically does not hold in general by considering $H = \mathbf{C}^2$ and

$$T = \begin{bmatrix} 0 & n \\ 0 & 0 \end{bmatrix}$$

on H, i.e., find $\|T\|$ and $r(T)$.

4. a. Given $T \in \mathcal{B}(H)$ with $T = T^*$, prove that T is positive $\Longleftrightarrow$ the image $\hat{T}$ of T under the Gelfand map is a nonnegative function. Hint for $\Longleftarrow$: Use the method of proof in Theorem 6.17 to obtain a nonnegative function $\hat{S} \in \mathcal{C}(\sigma(T))$ such that $(\hat{S})^2 = \hat{T}$ and then argue that $\langle Tx, x \rangle \geq 0$.

  b. Prove that every self-adjoint $T \in \mathcal{B}(H)$ can be uniquely expressed in the form $T = T_1 - T_2$ where T_1 and T_2 are positive and $T_1 T_2 = T_2 T_1 = 0$.

5. Let A denote the set of functions representable by absolutely convergent Fourier series:

$$A = \{f: [0, 2\pi) \to \mathbf{C}: f(\theta) = \sum_{n=-\infty}^{\infty} \alpha_n e^{in\theta} \quad \text{and}$$

$$\|f\| = \sum_{n=-\infty}^{\infty} |\alpha_n| < \infty \}.$$

  a. Show that with operations defined pointwise A is a commutative B^* algebra with identity. Hints: Given $f, g \in A$ with coefficients $\{\alpha_n\}$ and $\{\beta_n\}$, show that fg has coefficients $\{\gamma_n\}$ where

$$\gamma_n = \sum_{k=-\infty}^{\infty} \alpha_k \beta_{n-k} \text{ and show that } \sum_n |\gamma_n| < \infty \text{ by using}$$

$$\sum_n \sum_k |\alpha_k \beta_{n-k}| = \sum_k |\alpha_k| \sum_n |\beta_{n-k}|.$$

Argue that completeness of A follows from completeness of l^1.

b. Prove that every $\theta \in [0, 2\pi)$ gives rise to a continuous algebra homomorphism $h_\theta : A \to \mathbf{C}$ defined by $h_\theta(f) = f(\theta)$.

c. Given $\theta \in [0, 2\pi)$ argue that $M_\theta \in \mathfrak{M}$, the maximal ideal space of A, and conclude that A is semisimple.

6. Using the notation and results of Problem 5, let $M \in \mathfrak{M}$ and let $h: A \to A/M \cong \mathbf{C}$ be the corresponding algebra homomorphism. We wish to show that $h = h_{\theta_0}$ for some $\theta_0 \in [0, 2\pi)$ and hence that $\mathfrak{M}$ " $=$ " $[0, 2\pi)$.

a. Let $\alpha = h(f)$ where $f(\theta) = e^{i\theta}$ and argue that $|\alpha| = 1$. Hint: Recall (proof of Lemma 6.9d) that $\|h\| \leq 1$ and note that $h(f^{-1}) = 1/\alpha$.

b. Choose $\theta_0 \in [0, 2\pi)$ such that $e^{i\theta_0} = \alpha$ and argue that $h = h_{\theta_0}$ by showing that for every $g \in A$, $h(g) = g(\theta_0)$. Conclude that $\mathfrak{M}$ " $=$ " $[0, 2\pi)$. Hint: Since h is an algebra homomorphism, the above is true for finite sums.

c. Prove that $\sigma(g) = \text{range}(g)$ for every $g \in A$. Hint: $\lambda \in \sigma(g) \Rightarrow \hat{g}(M) = 0$ for some $M \in \mathfrak{M}$. But $\hat{g}(M) = h_\theta(g) = g(\theta)$ for some θ.

d. Prove Weiner's theorem: $g \in A$ and g nowhere $0 \Rightarrow 1/g \in A$.

References

1. G. F. Simmons, *Introduction to Topology and Modern Analysis*. New York: McGraw-Hill, 1963.

2. J. L. Kelley and I. Namioka, *Linear Topological Spaces*. Princeton, New Jersey: Van Nostrand Reinhold, 1963.

3. A. C. Zaanen, *An Introduction to the Theory of Integration*. Amsterdam: North-Holland, 1961.

4. A. Wilansky, *Functional Analysis*. New York: Ginn (Blaisdell), 1964.

5. J. Horvath, An introduction to distributions, *Amer. Math. Monthly* **77** (1970), 227–240.

6. F. Treves, Applications of distributions to PDE theory, *Amer. Math. Monthly* **77** (1970), 241–248.

7. K. Yosida, *Functional Analysis*. Berlin: Springer-Verlag, 1966.

8. J. Horvath, *Topological Vector Spaces and Distributions*. Reading, Massachusetts: Addison-Wesley, 1966.

9. N. Dunford and J. T. Schwartz, *Linear Operators*, Part I. New York: Wiley (Interscience), 1958.

10. C. Goffman and D. Waterman, Some aspects of Fourier series, *Amer. Math. Monthly* **77** (1970), 119–132.

11. A. Wilansky, Life without T_2, *Amer. Math. Monthly* **77** (1970), 157–161.

12. W. Rudin, *Real and Complex Analysis*. New York: McGraw-Hill, 1966.

13. L. H. Loomis, *An Introduction to Abstract Harmonic Analysis*. Princeton, New Jersey: Van Nostrand Reinhold, 1953.

14. P. Halmos, *A Hilbert Space Problem Book*. Princeton, New Jersey: Van Nostrand Reinhold, 1967.

15. D. P. Gillespie, *A Quantum Mechanics Primer*. New York and London: Intext Educational Publishers, 1970.

16. B. Cline, *Men Who Made a New Physics*. New York: New American Library, 1969.

17. S. Goldberg, *Unbounded Linear Operators*. New York: McGraw-Hill, 1966.

18. E. Hille and R. Phillips, *Functional Analysis and Semigroups*. Providence, Rhode Island: American Mathematical Society, 1957.

19. C. E. Rickart, *General Theory of Banach Algebras*. Princeton, New Jersey: Van Nostrand Reinhold, 1960.

20.   M. Reed and B. Simon, *Functional Analysis*. New York and London: Academic Press, 1972.

21.   P. Halmos, What does the spectral theorem say?, *Amer. Math. Monthly* **70** (1963), 241–247.

Index